Acts 4:13. 29

Now Lord) ---

TO SPEAK YOUR WORD WITH GREAT BOLDNESS.

30 STRETCH OUT YOUR HAND TO HEAL AND PERFORM

SIGNS AND WONDERS THROUGH THE NAME OF YOUR

SERVANT JESUS....

THE MEANING OF LIFE IS THE MYSTERY OF LOVE

THAT WHICH WE PRAY FOR
HELP US TO DO

1O-MINUTE
DIARY 2O17

CATHOLIC TRUTH SOCIETY
PUBLISHERS TO THE HOLY SEE

HOW TO USE THIS DIARY

D o you struggle to spend time with God every day? Maybe you want to read the Bible more often, but find yourself putting it off because you can't find the time. Or perhaps you forget about spending time in prayer, at least until you're ready for bed. You desire an intimate relationship with God, but aren't sure how to maintain it.

If any of this sounds familiar, then this resource is for you.

The *10-Minute Diary* has two essential functions. It is designed (1) to support your daily management of tasks, appointments and events, as well as (2) to help you to take ten minutes out of your busy day to meditate on God's Word.

Following the four principal stages of Lectio Divina (read, meditate, pray and act), you will be guided by scripture scholar Fr Javier Ruiz Ortiz through a bible reading each week, helping you to encounter God through the text. See the key guide across for more information on how to proceed through each of the stages.

You can choose to do the exercise each day or simply once a week. You may be surprised that you find new meanings and messages each time you read and meditate on a passage.

In addition to the Lectio Divina this diary also includes a collection of prayers to help you through many difficult situations. These prayers were kindly provided by the Poor Clare Sisters of Galway in Ireland.

Finally, we have included a map of the world featuring some of the world's pilgrimage sites. It can be used by those who either figuratively or quite literally wish to go on a spiritual journey. We've also included other diary-related material too.

So now there's nothing left to do but to take ten minutes, turn the page and simply relax with God.

Key Guide

a. Read:
What does the text say? While a bible commentary is not compulsory, you may find that it helps you to understand the context better.

b. Meditate:
What is God saying to me through the text? At this point, you can ask yourself whether there is something that God might want to reveal to you through the passage.

c. Pray:
After meditating on the Gospel, say the simple prayer and ask for the strength of the Holy Spirit to put the light received from reading and meditating on the passage into practice. You can also add to the prayer by telling God about your own feelings. Remember, God can handle any emotions you may have.

d. Act:
What do I want to do, based on my prayer? Prayer should move us to action, even if it simply makes us more aware of the presence of others. Why not adopt the action suggested at the end of each section? They are designed to help you to put into practice the Word ('lesson') received that day.

PERSONAL NOTES

Name: _____

Address: _____

_____

Tel.: _____ Fax No.: _____

Mobile: _____

Email: _____

In case of emergency please contact:

Name: _____

Address: _____

_____

Tel. Home: _____

Tel. Work: _____

Mobile: _____

Doctor: _____

Tel.: _____

Blood Group: _____

Allergies: _____

_____

National Insurance No.: _____

Car Registration No.: _____

Passport No.: _____

NOTABLE DATES

January
1   New Year's Day
2   Bank Holiday
3   Bank Holiday (Scotland)

February
14 St Valentine's Day
28 St David's Day

March
1   Ash Wednesday
17 St Patrick's Day (Bank Holiday, Ireland)
26 Mothering Sunday
26 British Summer Time begins
    - clocks go forward

April
14 Good Friday
16 Easter Sunday
17 Bank Holiday (excluding Scotland)
24 St George's Day

May
1   Early May Bank Holiday
29 Spring Bank Holiday (excluding
    Rep. of Ireland)

June
5   Bank Holiday (Rep. of Ireland)
18 Father's Day

July
12 Bank Holiday (Northern Ireland)
    [Battle of the Boyne]

August
7   Summer Bank Holiday (Scotland and
    Rep. of Ireland)
28 Summer Bank Holiday (excluding
    Scotland and Rep. of Ireland)

September
17 Home Mission Day

October
29 British Summer Time ends
    - clocks go back
30 Bank Holiday (Rep. of Ireland)
31 Halloween

November
12 Remembrance Sunday
30 St Andrew's Day (Bank Holiday, Scotland)

December
25 Christmas Day
26 Boxing Day

Roman Catholic Holy Days of Obligation

6 January	Epiphany of the Lord (Ireland)
8 January	Epiphany of the Lord (England, Wales and Scotland)
17 March	St Patrick (Ireland)
25 May	Ascension (Scotland)
28 May	Ascension (England, Wales and Ireland)
29 June	St Peter and St Paul
15 August	Assumption
1 November	All Saints
8 December	Immaculate Conception (Ireland)
25 December	Christmas Day

SPECIAL DATES

January

February

March

April

May

June

SPECIAL DATES

July

August

September

October

November

December

read

MARY, MOTHER OF GOD

The shepherds hurried away to Bethlehem and found Mary and Joseph, and the baby lying in the manger. When they saw the child they repeated what they had been told about him, and everyone who heard it was astonished at what the shepherds had to say. As for Mary, she treasured all these things and pondered them in her heart. And the shepherds went back glorifying and praising God for all they had heard and seen; it was exactly as they had been told.

When the eighth day came and the child was to be circumcised, they gave him the name Jesus, the name the angel had given him before his conception.

Luke 2:16-21

meditate

As we contemplate the mystery of God made man in the son of Mary, there are two attitudes we are called to have: Mary's and the shepherds'. Mary gazes in love and keeps things in her heart: an image of prayer. The shepherds spread the Good News of the birth of Jesus.

God of all tenderness, in your Son you have shown us that you are close to our needs; give me the spirit to remember you at all times and to share with others the good news of your birth.

act

You might want to share with someone the meaning of these days of Christmas – not only as a time for the family, but also as a time to remember that God entered our lives and wants to share these days with us.

JANUARY

The future starts today, not tomorrow.

1
SUN

CLONARD MASS

✤ Solemnity of Mary, The Holy Mother of God; New Year's Day

2
MON

BARBARA NO 1 AT HOME

THE WITNESS FOR THE PROSECUTION
BBC

Bank Holiday

3
TUES

HAIR CUT.

MoS WALK HOME

HALL painted

Bank Holiday (Scotland)

Sunday ✤	**Monday**	**Tuesday**	**Wednesday**	**Thursday**	**Friday**	**Saturday**
Numbers 6:22-27	1 John 2:22-28	1 John 2:29-3:6	1 John 3:7-10	1 John 3:11-21	1 John 5:5-13	1 John 5:14-21
Galatians 4:4-7	John 1:19-28	John 1:29-34	John 1:35-42	John 1:43-51	Mark 1:6-11 or	John 2:1-11
Luke 2:16-21					Luke 3:23-38	

4 WED

MAC DESKTOP
DELIVERED AND
WORKING.

5 THU

J.H. SMITH
FOR MAC BOOK.
WALKED BACK

6 FRI

HOLY COMMUNION

TIM BACK AT ALi's

Epiphany of the Lord (Ireland)

7 SAT

TIM & MEL
TALKING THINGS OVER

read

THE EPIPHANY

After Jesus had been born at Bethlehem in Judaea during the reign of King Herod, some wise men came to Jerusalem from the east. 'Where is the infant king of the Jews?' they asked. 'We saw his star as it rose and have come to do him homage.' When King Herod heard this he was perturbed, and so was the whole of Jerusalem. He called together all the chief priests and the scribes of the people, and enquired of them where the Christ was to be born. 'At Bethlehem in Judaea,' they told him 'for this is what the prophet wrote:

> And you, Bethlehem, in the land of Judah
> you are by no means least among the leaders of Judah,
> for out of you will come a leader
> who will shepherd my people Israel.'

Then Herod summoned the wise men to see him privately. He asked them the exact date on which the star had appeared, and sent them on to Bethlehem. 'Go and find out all about the child,' he said 'and when you have found him, let me know, so that I too may go and do him homage'. Having listened to what the king had to say, they set out. And there in front of them was the star they had seen rising; it went forward and halted over the place where the child was. The sight of the star filled them with delight, and going into the house they saw the child with his mother Mary, and falling to their knees they did him homage. Then, opening their treasures, they offered him gifts of gold and frankincense and myrrh. But they were warned in a dream not to go back to Herod, and returned to their own country by a different way.

Matthew 2:1-12

meditate

Our God is the God of surprises. Like the Magi, many times we look for God in the obvious places but sometimes he is not there. Even when we find him, we need to change the way we look, so that we can recognise him not only in nice, comfortable places, but also in the humility of a stable.

pray

Heavenly Father, light of the nations,

you wanted to share in the humility

of life with us; give me a desire to look

for you and open my eyes so that

I recognise you when you come my way.

act

With their gifts, the Magi recognised that Jesus was king, God and a human being. Think of an action whereby you acknowledge him as such in your life.

JANUARY

Wise men still seek him.

8
SUN

TRYING TO ACTIVATE
NOW TV on 17AC

⁜ Epiphany of the Lord; Baptism of the Lord (Ireland)

9
MON

Lunch Sainsburys
17AC NOW can use NOW TV

⁜ Baptism of the Lord (England, Wales and Scotland)

10
TUES

Blood for PSA

Sunday ⁜
Isaiah 60:1-6
Ephesians 3:2-3, 5-6
Matthew 2:1-12

Monday ⁜
Isaiah 42:1-4, 6-7
Acts 10:34-38
Matthew 3:13-17

Tuesday
Hebrews 2:5-12
Mark 1:21-28

Wednesday
Hebrews 2:14-18
Mark 1:29-39

Thursday
Hebrews 3:7-14
Mark 1:40-45

Friday
Hebrews 4:1-5, 11
Mark 2:1-12

Saturday
Hebrews 4:12-16
Mark 2:13-17

11
WED

Jayne

12
THU

Marie

Michael

Library M/S.

13
FRI

Sainsburry   Ali

14
SAT

Tim   A&E   Hyperventalating

After phoning Mel

Discharged around 11pm

read

SECOND SUNDAY IN ORDINARY TIME

Seeing Jesus coming towards him, John said, 'Look, there is the lamb of God that takes away the sin of the world. This is the one I spoke of when I said: A man is coming after me who ranks before me because he existed before me. I did not know him myself, and yet it was to reveal him to Israel that I came baptising with water.' John also declared, 'I saw the Spirit coming down on him from heaven like a dove and resting on him. I did not know him myself, but he who sent me to baptise with water had said to me, "The man on whom you see the Spirit come down and rest is the one who is going to baptise with the Holy Spirit." Yes, I have seen and I am the witness that he is the Chosen One of God.'

John 1:29-34

meditate

John the Baptist's ministry was to point out the presence of Jesus to his contemporaries. Today Jesus is still present in our lives, many times unbeknownst to us. Who reveals his presence and actions to you? How do you point him out to others?

pray

Lord, open my eyes to you passing through my life. May your actions show your goodness to me and to those I come in contact with, so that many may come to meet you, alive in their lives.

act

Acknowledge the person who has been John the Baptist for you. Think also who could you lead to Christ, pointing out his presence in the events of his or her life.

JANUARY

Discovering vocation does not mean scrambling toward some prize just beyond my reach but accepting the treasure of true self I already possess.

THOMAS MERTON

15 SUN

ALL CAME FOR CHAT ABOUT TIM
/HAD REACTION BUT OK

16 MON

SAINSBURYS with ALI lunch
Discussed Tim - He + Mel finished.
He depressed - DIAZAPEM

17 TUES

HALF MIRTAZAPINE
PHSYCATRIST ALL good -
MAKE APPT TO SEE DOC ABOUT
TIREDNESS
TAZ RANG TO ASK IF ID LIKE TO GO
TO BRICKS

18
WED

FIONA RIP.

19
THU

M₀S
WALK BACK
RESTORED MAC

20
FRI

Sainsbury with Ali

21
SAT

FACETIME NAZ

read

THIRD SUNDAY IN ORDINARY TIME

Hearing that John had been arrested Jesus went back to Galilee, and leaving Nazareth he went and settled in Capernaum, a lakeside town on the borders of Zebulun and Naphtali. In this way the prophecy of Isaiah was to be fulfilled:

Land of Zebulun! Land of Naphtali!
Way of the sea on the far side of Jordan,
Galilee of the nations!
The people that lived in darkness
has seen a great light;
on those who dwell in the land and shadow of death
a light has dawned.

From that moment Jesus began his preaching with the message, 'Repent, for the kingdom of heaven is close at hand.'

Matthew 4:12-17
(Longer form *Matthew* 4:12-23)

meditate

Jesus changes Peter, Andrew, John and James' activity by giving it a new meaning. They continue to be fishermen but, after their encounter with Jesus, they will be another sort of fishermen. Even today Jesus calls men and women to use their skills and activities to spread the Gospel.

pray

Lord, as you pass by in my life and call me to share in your mission by using my skills, let me be radical in following you and in spreading the Gospel among the people I encounter.

act

The first disciples were called in pairs. You might want to speak to a colleague or friend in your trade and think of a way of putting across the Christian message.

JANUARY

*Every disability conceals a vocation, if only we can find it,
which will 'turn the necessity to glorious gain'.*

C. S. LEWIS

22
SUN

23
MON

9.30 CARMEL.

Got up late & reappointed.

24
TUES

Y & S walked there & back

25
WED

Dr Naaman
DRI Blood Test
Continue medicine

✣ Conversion of St Paul, Apostle

26
THU

Randhir 3.00

27
FRI

Ali Holy Communion Sainsburys.

28
SAT

Marion
Great chat
Fiona's Foundation

read

Seeing the crowds, Jesus went up the hill. There he sat down and was joined by his disciples. Then he began to speak. This is what he taught them:

'How happy are the poor in spirit:
theirs is the kingdom of heaven.
Happy the gentle:
they shall have the earth for their heritage.
Happy those who mourn:
they shall be comforted.
Happy those who hunger and thirst for what is right:
they shall be satisfied.
Happy the merciful:
they shall have mercy shown them.
Happy the pure in heart:
they shall see God.
Happy the peacemakers:
they shall be called sons of God.
Happy those who are persecuted in the cause of right:
theirs is the kingdom of heaven.

'Happy are you when people abuse you and persecute you and speak all kinds of calumny against you on my account. Rejoice and be glad, for your reward will be great in heaven.'

Matthew 5:1-12

meditate

We look for happiness in our lives. All our actions point to this end, and even when we miss the target happiness is what we want. Jesus gives us nine ways to find blessedness and happiness; nine ways in which to rejoice. These are perhaps not our ways but God's ways, which are higher than ours – deeper than we can imagine.

pray

Lord of blessedness, show me the way to the path of true happiness. May I rejoice when I am poor, gentle, merciful, pure in heart, working for peace and persecuted for your cause. Assure me that my reward is close at hand.

act

We are the people of the beatitudes. This means we are both called to rejoice and to make others rejoice. Consider looking for an occasion when you can assist others in their path to happiness.

JANUARY

It is better to be a child of God than king of the whole world.

St Aloysius Gonzaga

29
SUN

TRAINERS DELIVERED

with Ali to Sainsbury.
Setraline reduced to 50mg

30
MON

Sainsbury with Ali

TRAINERS DELIVERED

31
TUES

Sunday
Zephaniah 2:3, 3:12-13
1 Corinthians 1:26-31
Matthew 5:1-12

Monday
Hebrews 11:32-40
Mark 5:1-20

Tuesday
Hebrews 12:1-4
Mark 5:21-43

Wednesday
Hebrews 12:4-7, 11-15
Mark 6:1-6

Thursday ✛
Malachi 3:1-4
Hebrews 2:14-18
Luke 2:22-40

Friday
Hebrews 13:1-8
Mark 6:14-29

Saturday
Hebrews 13:15-17,
20-21
Mark 6:30-34

FEBRUARY

1
WED

½ S
Bus in
WALK BACK

2
THU

3
FRI

PSA result fine
MARIE + STEPHEN on PHONE
½ S

4
SAT

6 NATIONS
SCOTLAND BEAT IRELAND

February

W	T	F	S	S	M	T	W	T	F	S	S	M	T	W	T	F	S	S	M	T	W	T	F	S	S	M	T
1	2	3	4	5	6	7	8	9	10	11	12	13	14	15	16	17	18	19	20	21	22	23	24	25	26	27	28

read

Jesus said to his disciples: 'You are the salt of the earth. But if salt becomes tasteless, what can make it salty again? It is good for nothing, and can only be thrown out to be trampled underfoot by men.

'You are the light of the world. A city built on a hill-top cannot be hidden. No one lights a lamp to put it under a tub; they put it on the lamp-stand where it shines for everyone in the house. In the same way your light must shine in the sight of men, so that, seeing your good works, they may give the praise to your Father in heaven.'

Matthew 5:13-16

meditate

Everyone likes to be praised and thanked for what they do; for how they behave; for their work. The Christian knows that the good actions he or she performs come ultimately from God to whom all praise and thanksgiving belong. Hence Jesus says, let people seeing your good works give praise to your Father in heaven.

pray

Heavenly Father to whom all praise is due, you are the only one deserving all thanksgiving: purify my inner intentions, so that in all I say and do the glory be given to you.

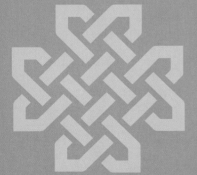

act

St Paul invites us to season our conversations with salt – meaning, not to use harmful words. Try to avoid using words that destroy the other person. Instead, make comments which will build him or her up.

FEBRUARY

All the darkness in the world cannot extinguish the light of a single candle.

ATTRIBUTED TO ST FRANCIS OF ASSISI

5
SUN

WALES BEAT ITALY

6
MON

SAINSBURYS

ALL LOST KEYS

TAXI HOME

BREADSALL

KEYS HANDED IN SO ALL OK

7
TUES

8 WED

12. 50   DR NORMAN   TAXI
                WALKED BACK

NEW TABS FOR NAUSEA etc

9 THU

10 FRI

SAINSBURY   1/2 S SHOP
                ALI

11 SAT

IRELAND BEAT ITALY
ENGLAND BEAT FRANCE

read

Jesus said to his disciples: 'For I tell you, if your virtue goes no deeper than that of the scribes and Pharisees, you will never get into the kingdom of heaven.

'You have learnt how it was said to our ancestors: You must not kill; and if anyone does kill he must answer for it before the court. But I say this to you: anyone who is angry with his brother will answer for it before the court.

'You have learnt how it was said: You must not commit adultery. But I say this to you: if a man looks at a woman lustfully, he has already committed adultery with her in his heart.

'Again, you have learnt how it was said to our ancestors: You must not break your oath, but must fulfil your oaths to the Lord. But I say this to you: do not swear at all. All you need say is "Yes" if you mean yes, "No" if you mean no; anything more than this comes from the evil one.'

Matthew 5:20-22, 27-28, 33-34, 37
(Longer form *Matthew* 5:17-37)

meditate

Every human action has two levels: the physical acts and the motivations which drive those actions. One flows into the other; they influence each other. Jesus says that evil comes from the heart, from our motivations; hence his message goes deep into the human heart so that actions get transformed.

pray

God of mercy and compassion, you know
the inner thoughts of the human heart;
you search the innermost parts of our
being. Enkindle in me the desire to change
so that what I profess with my lips may
reflect what I do with my actions.

act

Jesus invites us to be true to our words.
You might examine the words you use and
make sure that they are what you mean.

FEBRUARY

Don't let the sun go down on your family without having made your peace. It's not easy, but you have to do it. It will help to make life so much more beautiful.

POPE FRANCIS

12
SUN

FRANCE BEAT SCOTLAND.

13
MON

Tim getting the car fixed — again

14
TUES

FR JOHN
ABSOLUTION — Holy Communion
Good CHAT re fiona Foundation.
WILKO SAINSBURYS

✠ SS Cyril, Monk, and Methodius, Bishop; St Valentine's Day

Sunday	**Monday**	**Tuesday** ✠	**Wednesday**	**Thursday**	**Friday**	**Saturday**
Ecclesiasticus 15:15-20	Genesis 4:1-15, 25	Acts 13:46-49	Genesis 8:6-13, 20-22	Genesis 9:1-13	Genesis 11:1-9	Hebrews 11:1-7
1 Corinthians 2:6-10	Mark 8:11-13	Luke 10:1-9	Mark 8:22-26	Mark 8:27-33	Mark 8:34 – 9:1	Mark 9:2-13
Matthew 5:17-37						

FEBRUARY

15
WED

16
THU

Sainsburys. Bus there & back

Optical Express Specs fixed

17
FRI

18
SAT

February

W	T	F	S	S	M	T	W	T	F	S	S	M	T	W	T	F	S	S	M	T	W	T	F	S	S	M	T
1	2	3	4	5	6	7	8	9	10	11	12	13	14	15	16	17	18	19	20	21	22	23	24	25	26	27	28

read

Jesus said to his disciples: 'You have learnt how it was said: Eye for eye and tooth for tooth. But I say this to you: offer the wicked man no resistance. On the contrary, if anyone hits you on the right cheek, offer him the other as well; if a man takes you to law and would have your tunic, let him have your cloak as well. And if anyone orders you to go one mile, go two miles with him. Give to anyone who asks, and if anyone wants to borrow, do not turn away.

'You have learnt how it was said: You must love your neighbour and hate your enemy. But I say this to you: love your enemies and pray for those who persecute you; in this way you will be sons of your Father in heaven, for he causes his sun to rise on bad men as well as good, and his rain to fall on honest and dishonest men alike. For if you love those who love you, what right have you to claim any credit? Even the tax collectors do as much, do they not? And if you save your greetings for your brothers, are you doing anything exceptional? Even the pagans do as much, do they not? You must therefore be perfect just as your heavenly Father is perfect.'

Matthew 5:38-48

meditate

The normal reaction to receiving injustice or being subjected to evil is to repay in the same manner. St Francis of Assisi blesses God for those who forgive for the love of him; for those who, knowing how much they have been forgiven, can be merciful to others and patient with themselves.

pray

Father, whose nature is to be slow to anger and abounding in love, open my eyes to the way you have treated me so that I may choose reconciliation over vengeance and forgiveness over revenge.

act

Think of someone who has done a wrong to you. Following Jesus' invitation in the Gospel, pray for them – wishing them God's blessings. Perhaps try to do good to them, if this is possible.

FEBRUARY

Pray as you can. Don't try to pray as you can't.

ABBOT JOHN CHAPMAN

19 SUN

DOWNLOADING BIBLE AUDIBLE
NEW TESTAMENT STUDY

20 MON

IZZIE'S BIRTHDAY 1998

DENTIST. 1.30
Rearranged for Next mon
~~had my wallet~~
LOST MY WALLET

21 TUES

BANK FOR CASH
COUNCIL HOUSE for BUS PASS
M2S

Sunday	Monday	Tuesday	Wednesday ✠	Thursday	Friday	Saturday
Leviticus 19:1-2, 17-18	Ecclesiasticus 1:1-10	Ecclesiasticus 2:1-11	1 Peter 5:1-4	Ecclesiasticus 5:1-8	Ecclesiasticus 6:5-17	Ecclesiasticus 17:1-15
1 Corinthians 3:16-23	Mark 9:14-29	Mark 9:30-37	Matthew 16:13-19	Mark 9:41-50	Mark 10:1-12	Mark 10:13-16
Matthew 5:38-48						

22
WED

JAYNÉ FOUND TEETH!

DEBIT CARD ARRIVED

ORDERED WALLET

✣ Chair of St Peter, Apostle

23
THU

24
FRI

HOLY COMMUNION

SAINSBURYS

25
SAT

LAPTOP ARRIVED.

February	W	T	F	S	S	M	T	W	T	F	S	S	M	T	W	T	F	S	S	M	T	W	T	F	S	S	M	T
	1	2	3	**4**	**5**	6	7	8	9	10	**11**	**12**	13	14	15	16	17	**18**	**19**	20	21	22	23	24	**25**	**26**	27	28

read

Jesus said to his disciples: 'No one can be the slave of two masters: he will either hate the first and love the second, or treat the first with respect and the second with scorn. You cannot be the slave both of God and of money.

'That is why I am telling you not to worry about your life and what you are to eat, nor about your body and how you are to clothe it. Surely life means more than food, and the body more than clothing! Look at the birds in the sky. They do not sow or reap or gather into barns; yet your heavenly Father feeds them. Are you not worth much more than they are? Can any of you, for all his worrying, add one single cubit to his span of life? And why worry about clothing? Think of the flowers growing in the fields; they never have to work or spin; yet I assure you that not even Solomon in all his regalia was robed like one of these. Now if that is how God clothes the grass in the field which is there today and thrown into the furnace tomorrow, will he not much more look after you, you men of little faith? So do not worry; do not say, "What are we to eat? What are we to drink? How are we to be clothed?" It is the pagans who set their hearts on all these things. Your heavenly Father knows you need them all. Set your hearts on his kingdom first, and on his righteousness, and all these other things will be given you as well. So do not worry about tomorrow; tomorrow will take care of itself. Each day has enough trouble of its own.'

Matthew 6:24-34

meditate

God is a Father who has his children's interests at heart. He knows about our desires and foresees what we need. If we truly believe in him, we will trust that he has our good as his main goal. Trust is meant not only for spiritual things but for material goods as well.

pray

God of providence, all creatures look to you
to provide for them; open your hand and fill
them with your goodness; keep our eyes fixed
on you and our hearts set on your kingdom,
so that we may entrust our daily cares to you.

act

Relying on God means trusting that he will provide money, food and clothes. Consider giving some of these things to those in need, and experience how God rewards you a hundred times over.

FEBRUARY

*Let nothing disturb you. Let nothing frighten you. All things pass
away: God never changes. Patience obtains all things. Those who
have God find they lack nothing; God alone is enough.*

St Teresa of Avila

26
SUN

27
MON

Sainsburys
WITH ALI

ORDERED Headphones AMAZON
BATTERY FOR RADIO

28
TUES

MEDS DELIVERED.

SERTRALINE STOPPED

MIRTAZAPINE REDUCED FROM 30
TO 15mg.

✠ St David, Bishop

1 WED

BLUETOOTH HEADSET

BUS PASS

HAIRCUT

M2S WALKED BACK

✣ Ash Wednesday

2 THU

3 FRI

SAINSBURYS WITH ALI

4 SAT

ALI TO BRIARS.

MAZ IZZIE ELLIE & ME TO HARVESTER
PRIDE PARK AND THEN TO MARIES.

March	W	T	F	S	S	M	T	W	T	F	S	S	M	T	W	T	F	S	S	M	T	W	T	F	S	S	M	T	W	T	F
	1	2	3	**4**	**5**	6	7	8	9	10	**11**	**12**	13	14	15	16	17	**18**	**19**	20	21	22	23	24	**25**	**26**	27	28	29	30	31

read

Jesus was led by the Spirit out into the wilderness to be tempted by the devil. He fasted for forty days and forty nights, after which he was very hungry, and the tempter came and said to him, 'If you are the Son of God, tell these stones to turn into loaves.' But he replied, 'Scripture says:

Man does not live on bread alone
but on every word that comes from the mouth of God.'

The devil then took him to the holy city and made him stand on the parapet of the Temple. 'If you are the Son of God' he said 'throw yourself down; for scripture says:

He will put you in his angels' charge,
and they will support you on their hands
in case you hurt your foot against a stone.'

Jesus said to him, 'Scripture also says:

You must not put the Lord your God to the test.'

Next, taking him to a very high mountain, the devil showed him all the kingdoms of the world and their splendour. 'I will give you all these' he said, 'if you fall at my feet and worship me.' Then Jesus replied, 'Be off, Satan! For scripture says:

You must worship the Lord your God,
and serve him alone.'

Then the devil left him, and angels appeared and looked after him.

Matthew 4:1-11

meditate

Temptations, trials and difficulties are part of life and are absolutely necessary moments in our Christian discipleship when we must decide whether or not to follow Jesus. However, as St Paul reminds us, nobody is tempted beyond their strength. Because Christ has conquered sin, we are confident we can be victorious since we share in Jesus' triumph.

pray

God of all consolation, you do not push us beyond our limits; give me courage and fortitude when faced with temptations; increase my trust in you, in the knowledge that you have already defeated sin for me.

act

Angels came to serve Jesus at the moment of his trials. We are surrounded by people who are going through moments of trial in their lives. Consider how you could be an angel to serve and to help them pass through their struggles.

MARCH

The greatest temptations are not those that solicit our consent to obvious sin, but those that offer us great evils masking as the greatest goods.

THOMAS MERTON

5
SUN

6
MON

Nails

7
TUES

M₂S

WALKED BACK

8
WED

Jayne.

9
THU

Mr S

10
FRI

EVENING   SAINSBURYS WITH Ali

✠ St John Ogilvie, Priest and Martyr (Scotland)

11
SAT

ALL   LLANDUDNO

Chemist for fratidine
Walked here & back.

March	W	T	F	S	S	M	T	W	T	F	S	S	M	T	W	T	F	S	S	M	T	W	T	F	S	S	M	T	W	T	F
	1	2	3	4	5	6	7	8	9	10	11	12	13	14	15	16	17	18	19	20	21	22	23	24	25	26	27	28	29	30	31

read

Jesus took with him Peter and James and his brother John and led them up a high mountain where they could be alone. There in their presence he was transfigured; his face shone like the sun and his clothes became as white as the light. Suddenly Moses and Elijah appeared to them; they were talking with him. Then Peter spoke to Jesus. 'Lord,' he said 'it is wonderful for us to be here; if you wish, I will make three tents here, one for you, one for Moses and one for Elijah.' He was still speaking when suddenly a bright cloud covered them with shadow, and from the cloud there came a voice which said, 'This is my Son, the Beloved; he enjoys my favour. Listen to him.' When they heard this, the disciples fell on their faces, overcome with fear. But Jesus came up and touched them. 'Stand up,' he said 'do not be afraid.' And when they raised their eyes they saw no one but only Jesus.

As they came down from the mountain Jesus gave them this order. 'Tell no one about the vision until the Son of Man has risen from the dead.'

Matthew 17:1-9

meditate

Jesus climbs up a mountain with some of his friends, and there he is transfigured. This experience will help his disciples when they think of the same Jesus going up another mountain on his own to have his face disfigured. The only way of looking at the suffering Jesus is to contemplate his glory in our lives.

pray

God of power and might, upon
the mountain you reveal your glory
for all to see; remind me of the
glorious moments in which you are
plainly seen in my life, so that when
darkness and disappointment come,
I may still trust in you.

act

Jesus had a visit from Moses and Elijah
as he faced his passion. We all know
of people who are suffering and facing
challenges; think about visiting them or
giving them some sort of encouragement.

MARCH

12
SUN

ALI BACK FROM LLANDUDNO

13
MON

14
TUES

15 WED

PRINTERS AT SPOT CLOSED DOWN.

WALKED THERE & BACK
1/2 S.

16 THU

WILKINSONS FOR OIL FOR CUPBOARD DOOR.
TALC
SAINSBURY'S
WALKED BACK.

17 FRI

SAINSBURYS WITH ALI

ORDERED LAPTOP EBAY.

St Patrick, Bishop; Bank Holiday (Ireland)

18 SAT

IRELAND BEAT ENGLAND)

March

W	T	F	S	S	M	T	W	T	F	S	S	M	T	W	T	F	S	S	M	T	W	T	F	S	S	M	T	W	T	F
1	2	3	4	5	6	7	8	9	10	11	12	13	14	15	16	17	18	19	20	21	22	23	24	25	26	27	28	29	30	31

read

Jesus came to the Samaritan town called Sychar, near the land that Jacob gave to his son Joseph. Jacob's well is there and Jesus, tired by the journey, sat straight down by the well. It was about the sixth hour. When a Samaritan woman came to draw water, Jesus said to her, 'Give me a drink.' His disciples had gone into the town to buy food. The Samaritan woman said to him, 'What? You are a Jew and you ask me, a Samaritan for a drink?' – Jews in fact, do not associate with Samaritans. Jesus replied:

'If you only knew what God is offering
and who it is that is saying to you:
Give me a drink,
you would have been the one to ask,
and he would have given you living water.'

'Sir,' said the woman, 'give me some of that water, so that I may never get thirsty and never have to come here again to draw water.' 'Go and call your husband' said Jesus to her 'and come back here.' The woman answered, 'I have no husband.' He said to her, 'You are right to say, "I have no husband"; for although you have had five, the one you have now is not your husband. You spoke the truth there.' 'I see you are a prophet, sir' said the woman.

Short extract from *John* 4:5-42

meditate

All of us have a secret which we would rather not share. However, there is a great sense of freedom and relief when we meet someone we can share our full story with; someone who does not judge us. This is prayer: finding someone who knows us through and through and yet loves us all the same.

pray

All knowing and all loving God, you know everything about me and are the only one who can reveal my innermost secrets to me. Give me the simplicity to share my story with you so I may attain full knowledge of your love.

act

The Samaritan woman was an outcast, someone people avoided and most probably she did not speak to many people. You might try to make conversation with someone you are aware of who is in that situation.

MARCH

19
SUN

20
MON

Morrisons with Ali

Swopped Kindles.

✠ St Joseph, Spouse of the Blessed Virgin Mary

21
TUES

Sunday	**Monday** ✠	**Tuesday**	**Wednesday**	**Thursday**	**Friday**	**Saturday** ✠
Exodus 17:3-7	2 Samuel 7:4-5, 12-14, 16	Daniel 3:25, 34-43	Deuteronomy	Jeremiah 7:23-28	Hosea 14:2-10	Isaiah 7:10-14, 8:10
Romans 5:1-2, 5-8	Romans 4:13, 16-18, 22; Matthew	Matthew 18:21-35	4:1, 5-9	Luke 11:14-23	Mark 12:28-34	Hebrews 10:4-10
John 4:5-42	1:16, 18-21, 24 or Luke 2:41-51		Matthew 5:17-19			Luke 1:26-38

22
WED

23
THU

BARBARA TELL ME SHES

BARBARA TELLS ME SHE'S MOVING NEXT THURS

24
FRI

M²S. WALKED BACK.

25
SAT

✣ The Annunciation of the Lord

read

FOURTH SUNDAY OF LENT

As Jesus went along, he saw a man who had been blind from birth. He spat on the ground, made a paste with the spittle, put this over the eyes of the blind man and said to him, 'Go and wash in the Pool of Siloam' (a name that means 'sent'). So the blind man went off and washed himself, and came away with his sight restored.

His neighbours and people who earlier had seen him begging said, 'Isn't this the man who used to sit and beg?' Some said, 'Yes, it is the same one.' Others said, 'No, he only looks like him.' The man himself said, 'I am the man.'

They brought the man who had been blind to the Pharisees. It had been a sabbath day when Jesus made the paste and opened the man's eyes, so when the Pharisees asked him how he had come to see, he said, 'He put a paste on my eyes, and I washed, and I can see.' Then some of the Pharisees said, 'This man cannot be from God: he does not keep the sabbath.' Others said, 'How could a sinner produce signs like this?' And there was disagreement among them. So they spoke to the blind man again, 'What have you to say about him yourself, now that he has opened your eyes?' 'He is a prophet' replied the man.

'Are you trying to teach us,' they replied 'and you a sinner through and through, since you were born!' And they drove him away.

Jesus heard they had driven him away, and when he found him he said to him, 'Do you believe in the Son of Man?' 'Sir,' the man replied 'tell me who he is so that I may believe in him.' Jesus said, 'You are looking at him; he is speaking to you.' The man said, 'Lord, I believe', and worshipped him.

John 9:1, 6-9,13-17, 34-38
(Longer form *John* 9:1-41)

meditate

Some people think that evil happens to others as a way to punish them for previous misdemeanours. Jesus has a different outlook on life. Illnesses and health issues happen so that God's glory may be manifested. He might not cure us, but the greatest miracle is to accept a sickness and bear it patiently.

pray

God of light, open my eyes to see you acting in my life. Give me faith to wait for your intervention so that when you act I may recognise you, proclaim my faith in you and, in this way, lead others to praise your name.

act

The blind man was presented to Jesus by his disciples. Think of someone in difficulty you could present to Jesus or even invite them to trust in God.

MARCH

Start by doing what's necessary; then do what's possible; and suddenly you are doing the impossible.

ATTRIBUTED TO St Francis of Assisi

26
SUN

Sainsbury   shop   lunch
Cosco   photos

Mothering Sunday; British Summer Time begins – clocks go forward

27
MON

Adobe Acrobat.

28
TUES

We   Website   Renewed.
Booklets Revised

29 WED

ACROBAT 6.

with

WILKINSONS — OPTIE HOUSE
WALKED BACK.

30 THU

BARBARA MOVES to Sussex Green

31 FRI

SAINSBURYS WITH ALI.

PHOTOS FROM COSCO ALI DID THEY.

DAN HAS MOVED IN TO RAYS.

1 SAT

April

S S M T W T F S S M T W T F S S M T W T F S S M T W T F S S
1 2 3 4 5 6 7 8 9 10 11 12 13 14 15 16 17 18 19 20 21 22 23 24 25 26 27 28 29 30

read

The sisters sent this message to Jesus, 'Lord, the man you love is ill.' On receiving the message, Jesus said, 'This sickness will end not in death but in God's glory, and through it the Son of God will be glorified.'

Jesus loved Martha and her sister and Lazarus, yet when he heard that Lazarus was ill he stayed where he was for two more days before saying to the disciples, 'Let us go to Judaea.'

On arriving, Jesus found that Lazarus had been in the tomb for four days already. When Martha heard that Jesus had come she went to meet him. Mary remained sitting in the house. Martha said to Jesus, 'If you had been here, my brother would not have died, but I know that, even now, whatever you ask of God, he will grant you.' 'Your brother' said Jesus to her 'will rise again.' Martha said, 'I know he will rise again at the resurrection on the last day.' Jesus said:

'I am the resurrection and the life.
If anyone believes in me, even though he dies
he will live,
and whoever lives and believes in me
will never die.
Do you believe this?'

'Yes Lord,' she said 'I believe that you are the Christ, the Son of God, the one who was to come into this world.

[Jesus said], 'Lazarus, here! Come out!' The dead man came out, his feet and hands bound with bands of stuff and a cloth round his face.

Short extract from *John* 11:1-45

meditate

Jesus is a friend of families, and today we find him visiting one in a moment of distress. Both Martha and Mary bring the same request to Jesus. However, his response is different to each. We should not be put off if God does not answer our request immediately. He will when the time has come.

pray

God of the living, you call us to life and when our time is over, you call us back to you. Give me faith to persevere in my prayer of intercession, in certain knowledge that you will always do the best for me.

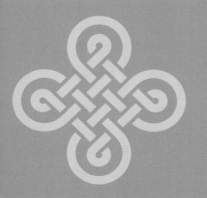

act

Jesus went to console his friends in a moment of bereavement. All of us are surrounded by people who have lost a loved one. Follow Jesus' example: be with them, sharing in their pain and speaking if you feel it is necessary.

APRIL

At any minute it is what we are and are doing, not what we plan to be and do that counts.

J. R. R. TOLKIEN

2
SUN

20 Min walk
Osenstons Rd.

3
MON

All Sainsburys

Working on Website & Books

4
TUES

Editing   Walking thro Vines
Pilgrimage of the Heart.

5
WED

Town
WALKED BACK.

6
THU

VISITED Marie & Stephen
Bus THERE & BACK.

7
FRI

Sainsbury with Ali
Aus/my TUBE FITTED.

8
SAT

£50 Win Grand National.
Walked to M&S & back.

April

S	S	M	T	W	T	F	S	S	M	T	W	T	F	S	S	M	T	W	T	F	S	S	M	T	W	T	F	S	S
1	2	3	4	5	6	7	8	9	10	11	12	13	14	15	16	17	18	19	20	21	22	23	24	25	26	27	28	29	30

read

At festival time it was the governor's practice to release a prisoner for the people, anyone they chose. Now there was at that time a notorious prisoner whose name was Barabbas. So when the crowd gathered, Pilate said to them,

O Which do you want me to release for you: Barabbas or Jesus who is called Christ?

N The chief priests and the elders, however, had persuaded the crowd to demand the release of Barabbas and the execution of Jesus.

N They all said:

C Let him be crucified!

N Then Pilate saw that he was making no impression, that in fact a riot was imminent. So he took some water, washed his hands in front of the crowd and said:

O I am innocent of this man's blood. It is your concern.

N Then he released Barabbas for them. He ordered Jesus to be first scourged and then handed over to be crucified.

N At that, the veil of the Temple was torn in two from top to bottom; the earth quaked; the rocks were split; the tombs opened and the bodies of many holy men rose from the dead, and these, after his resurrection, came out of the tombs, entered the Holy City and appeared to a number of people.

Meanwhile the centurion, together with the others guarding Jesus, had seen the earthquake and all that was taking place, and they were terrified and said:

C In truth this was a son of God.

Short extract from *Matthew* 27:11-54

meditate

There are many actors in the drama of Jesus' passion. As we read the familiar story, it is worth stopping and asking ourselves who we are in the story. Are we the disciples who run away? Are we the crowds who betray Jesus? Or perhaps the women who follow and help Jesus? All of us have a role to play.

pray

Lord Jesus, out of love for humanity you mounted the wood of the cross, while all along praying for those who assisted in your execution. Give me courage to place myself in this story and strength to stand by you.

act

At the centre of our faith stands the cross of Jesus. Some people find it offensive, but for us the cross is a sign of how much God loves us. Think of where you might place a cross in your house or place of work to remind you of this love.

APRIL

A wise man will make haste to forgive, because he knows the true value of time, and will not suffer it to pass away in unnecessary pain.

SAMUEL JOHNSON

9
SUN

Passion Sunday

10
MON

St Joes n Sainsburys
Fr John café doesn't look well

11
TUES

Clintons for Easter Cards

Passion Sunday
Isaiah 50:4-7
Philippians 2:6-11
Matthew 26:14 – 27:66

Monday
Isaiah 42:1-7
John 12:1-11

Tuesday
Isaiah 49:1-6
John 13:21-33, 36-38

Wednesday
Isaiah 50:4-9
Matthew 26:14-25

Maundy Thursday
Exodus 12:1-8, 11-14
1 Corinthians 11:23-26
John 13:1-15

Good Friday
Isaiah 52:13 – 53:12
Hebrews 4:14-16, 5:7-9
John 18:1 – 19:42

Holy Saturday
(Easter Vigil) Various readings, including Matthew 28:1-10

12
WED

Walking thro' the vines out for
printing

13
THU

WALKED   TO   POST OFFICE
AIR MAIL   CARD TO MICHAEL
      POSTED EASTER CARDS

Maundy Thursday

14
FRI

MAE RANG FROM I.O.W 3 children
THEY go sailing this PM
ALL GOOD
ALI CAME AFTER ST MARY'S
                    SERVICE

Good Friday; Bank Holiday

15
SAT

POST GOOD FRIDAY
Snow & Heavy

Holy Saturday

April

S S M T W T F S S M T W T F S S M T W T F S S M T W T F S S
1 2 3 4 5 6 7 8 9 10 11 12 13 14 15 16 17 18 19 20 21 22 23 24 25 26 27 28 29 30

read

EASTER SUNDAY

It was very early on the first day of the week and still dark, when Mary of Magdala came to the tomb. She saw that the stone had been moved away from the tomb and came running to Simon Peter and the other disciple, the one Jesus loved. 'They have taken the Lord out of the tomb' she said 'and we don't know where they have put him.'

So Peter set out with the other disciple to go to the tomb. They ran together, but the other disciple, running faster than Peter, reached the tomb first; he bent down and saw the linen cloths lying on the ground, but did not go in. Simon Peter who was following now came up, went right into the tomb, saw the linen cloths on the ground, and also the cloth that had been over his head; this was not with the linen cloths but rolled up in a place by itself. Then the other disciple who had reached the tomb first also went in; he saw and he believed. Till this moment they had failed to understand the teaching of scripture, that he must rise from the dead.

John 20:1-9

meditate

If you go to a tomb, the most usual thing is to find a body. Mary is surprised that the tomb is empty. She shares that perplexity with others. The Easter season invites us to place Jesus into the places of death in our life so that he may transform them into places that give life.

pray

God of life, you did not allow your only-begotten Son to experience the corruption of the tomb; grant me faith in the resurrection of Jesus and its power to change my life too.

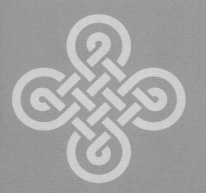

act

Mary of Magdala went away from the tomb to share what she had found with Peter. Think of ways in which you might share with someone the true meaning of Easter and the joy of the resurrection.

APRIL

*Just because we don't understand doesn't mean that
the explanation doesn't exist.*

MADELEINE L'ENGLE

16
SUN

Lovely lunch at Marics

✢ Easter Sunday

17
MON

PILGRIMAGE OF THE HEART
READY FOR PRINTING

£272

Bank Holiday (excluding Scotland)

18
TUES

£261

WALKING Thro The Vines ARRIVED

PILGRIMAGE OF THE HEART for printing

19 WED

WALKED TO M & S AND BACK

20 THU

NAILS DONE.
Pilgrimage of The Heart
delivered

21 FRI

Sainsburys with Ali.

22 SAT

Walked for 200/115

April

S S M T W T F S S M T W T F S S M T W T F S S M T W T F S S
1 2 3 4 5 6 7 8 9 10 11 12 13 14 15 16 17 18 19 20 21 22 23 24 25 26 27 28 29 30

read

In the evening of that same day, the first day of the week, the doors were closed in the room where the disciples were, for fear of the Jews. Jesus came and stood among them. He said to them, 'Peace be with you,' and showed them his hands and his side. The disciples were filled with joy when they saw the Lord, and he said to them again,

'Peace be with you. As the Father sent me, so am I sending you.'

After saying this he breathed on them and said:

'Receive the Holy Spirit. For those whose sins you forgive, they are forgiven; for those whose sins you retain, they are retained.'

Thomas, called the Twin, who was one of the Twelve, was not with them when Jesus came. When the disciples said, 'We have seen the Lord,' he answered, 'Unless I see the holes that the nails made in his hands and can put my finger into the holes they made, and unless I can put my hand into his side, I refuse to believe.' Eight days later the disciples were in the house again and Thomas was with them. The doors were closed, but Jesus came in and stood among them. 'Peace be with you,' he said. Then he spoke to Thomas, 'Put your finger here; look, here are my hands. Give me your hand; put it into my side. Doubt no longer but believe.' Thomas replied, 'My Lord and my God!'

Jesus said to him:

'You believe because you can see me. Happy are those who have not seen and yet believe.'

There were many other signs that Jesus worked and the disciples saw, but they are not recorded in this book. These are recorded so that you may believe that Jesus is the Christ, the Son of God, and that believing this you may have life through his name.

John 20:19-31

meditate

The risen Lord appears to his disciples giving them five precious gifts: joy, peace, mission, the Holy Spirit and the power to forgive sins. These extend to those who were not there. And, in Thomas, God wants us to rejoice in those gifts.

pray

Risen Lord, make me use wisely the gifts you provide, so that, in spreading the Gospel, many come to the blessedness of knowing and believing in you, even without having seen you.

act

Jesus invited Thomas to touch his wounds; when he did so, faith grew in Thomas. Christ's open wounds are available to us today in those who suffer. How can you reach out to some of them and heal those wounds?

APRIL

Faith is to believe what you do not yet see; the reward for this faith is to see what you believe.

St Augustine of Hippo

23
SUN

WALKED TO TOWN FOR COMPUTER PAPER.

24
MON

Sainsburys with Ali.

MEDICINE DELIVERED

✠ St George, Martyr (England)

25
TUES

ALI to MEDS.

✠ St Mark, Evangelist

Sunday	Monday (England) ✠	Monday (Wales & Scotland)	Tuesday ✠	Wednesday	Thursday	Friday	Saturday ✠
Acts 2:42-47	Revelation 12:10-12	Acts 4:23-31	Peter 5:5-14	Acts 5:17-26	Acts 5:27-33	Acts 5:34-42	1 John 1:5 – 2:2
1 Peter 1:3-9	John 15:18-21 or	John 3:1-8)	Mark 16:15-20	John 3:16-21	John 3:31-36	John 6:1-15	Matthew 11:25-30
John 20:19-31	15:1-8						

26
WED

M₂ S.

27
THU

WALKED

28
FRI

LIBRARY
WALKED BACK.

29
SAT

✠ St Catherine of Siena, Virgin and Doctor of the Church

April	S	S	M	T	W	T	F	S	S	M	T	W	T	F	S	S	M	T	W	T	F	S	S	M	T	W	T	F	S	S
	1	2	3	4	5	6	7	8	9	10	11	12	13	14	15	16	17	18	19	20	21	22	23	24	25	26	27	28	29	30

read

Two of the disciples of Jesus were on their way to a village called Emmaus, seven miles from Jerusalem, and they were talking together about all that had happened. Now as they talked this over, Jesus himself came up and walked by their side; but something prevented them from recognising him. He said to them, 'What matters are you discussing as you walk along?' They stopped short, their faces downcast.

Then one of them, called Cleopas, answered him, 'You must be the only person staying in Jerusalem who does not know the things that have been happening there these last few days.' 'What things?' he asked. 'All about Jesus of Nazareth' they answered 'who proved he was a great prophet by the things he said and did in the sight of God and of the whole people; and how our chief priests and our leaders handed him over to be sentenced to death, and had him crucified.

Then he said to them, 'You foolish men! So slow to believe the full message of the prophets! Was it not ordained that the Christ should suffer and so enter into his glory?' Then, starting with Moses and going through all the prophets, he explained to them the passages throughout the scriptures that were about himself.

When they drew near to the village to which they were going, he made as if to go on; but they pressed him to stay with them. 'It is nearly evening' they said 'and the day is almost over.' So he went in to stay with them. Now while he was with them at table, he took the bread and said the blessing; then he broke it and handed it to them. And their eyes were opened and they recognised him; but he had vanished from their sight. Then they said to each other, 'Did not our hearts burn within us as he talked to us on the road and explained the scriptures to us?'

Short extract from *Luke* 24:13-35

meditate

We often encounter disappointments in our life, and also in our experience of faith. We seem to have lost our faith. We need someone to help us enunciate the problems. Someone who helps us to interpret the things that have happened so that instead of having a heavy heart, our being may be kindled with love.

pray

Lord, you never abandon us on the journey of life. You are always close to us even when we cannot recognise you. Enkindle in my heart the desire to be with you so that I may set the world on fire with your love.

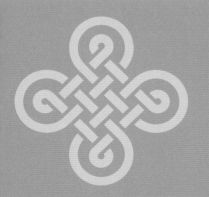

act

Jesus walked alongside the disciples, listening and asking leading questions so that they could tell their story. Do something similar with someone who needs to be listened to – not speaking much but listening lots.

APRIL – MAY

The best part of the journey is the surprise and wonder along the way.

KEN POIROT

30
SUN

WALKED   BATEMAN ST.

1
MON

BATEMAN ST.

EMAIL AU

Bank Holiday

2
TUES

HAIRCUT.

Sunday	Monday	Tuesday	Wednesday ✠	Thursday (England) ✠	Thursday (Wales & Scotland)	Friday	Saturday
Acts 2:14, 22-33	Acts 6:8-15	Acts 7:51 – 8:1	1 Corinthians 15:1-8	Acts 7:55-60	Acts 8:26-40	Acts 9:1-20	Acts 9:31-42
1 Peter 1:17-21	John 6:22-29	John 6:30-35	John 14:6-14	Matthew 10:17-20	John 6:44-51	John 6:52-59	John 6:60-69
Luke 24:13-35							

3
WED

ALI BACK TODAY

✛ SS Philip and James, Apostles

4
THU

NEW TESTAMENT (3) TO CATHEDRAL

✛ The Beatified Martyrs of England and Wales (England)

5
FRI

Sainsburys with Ali

6
SAT

ORDERED DAILY MISSAL REPLACING Fr Johns

May

M T W T F S S M T W T F S S M T W T F S S M T W T F S S M T W
1 2 3 4 5 **6 7** 8 9 10 11 12 **13 14** 15 16 17 18 19 **20 21** 22 23 24 25 26 **27 28** 29 30 31

read

FOURTH SUNDAY OF EASTER

Jesus said: 'I tell you most solemnly, anyone who does not enter the sheepfold through the gate, but gets in some other way is a thief and a brigand. The one who enters through the gate is the shepherd of the flock; the gatekeeper lets him in, the sheep hear his voice, one by one he calls his own sheep and leads them out. When he has brought out his flock, he goes ahead of them, and the sheep follow because they know his voice. They never follow a stranger but run away from him: they do not recognise the voice of strangers.'

Jesus told them this parable but they failed to understand what he meant by telling it to them.

So Jesus spoke to them again:

'I tell you most solemnly, I am the gate of the sheepfold. All others who have come are thieves and brigands; but the sheep took no notice of them. I am the gate. Anyone who enters through me will be safe: he will go freely in and out and be sure of finding pasture. The thief comes only to steal and kill and destroy. I have come so that they may have life and have it to the full.'

John 10:1-10

meditate

Jesus promises life, and life to the full. In speaking of this kind of life he requires his sheep to listen to him and not to trust the voice of strangers. In our lives we are bombarded by so many different voices. It is worth being still to listen for the right call in our lives.

pray

Good Shepherd, you lead us to restful waters and want us to follow you. Open my ears so I may listen to your voice and lead me to your green pastures, so that I may not be like a vagabond, following other shepherds.

act

We have so many distractions and follow so many different voices. So it is important to make some silence in our external life so we may hear what God is saying in our heart.

MAY

Every good man resists others in those points in which he resists himself.

St Augustine of Hippo

7
SUN

Tim to Milton Keynes to start new job
20 months since Ali has house to herself (Walked) Batoyaw ST & Back ⊘

8
MON

M & S

WALKED

9
TUES

DAILY MISSAL CAFÉ

17733/43/69

MAY

£270

10 WED

SPECSAVERS FOR NEW LEFT HEARING AID

M&S

WALKED BACK.

11 THU

EXHAUSTED FOR A COUPLE OF HOURS 20 MINS WALK & FELT BETTER.

12 FRI

AFTERNOON HOLY COMMUNION

SAINSBURYS WITH ALI

13 SAT

£264

May	M	T	W	T	F	S	S	M	T	W	T	F	S	S	M	T	W	T	F	S	S	M	T	W	T	F	S	S	M	T	W
	1	2	3	4	5	**6**	**7**	8	9	10	11	12	**13**	**14**	15	16	17	18	19	**20**	**21**	22	23	24	25	26	**27**	**28**	29	30	31

read

FIFTH SUNDAY OF EASTER

Jesus said to his disciples:

'Do not let your hearts be troubled. Trust in God still, and trust in me. There are many rooms in my Father's house; if there were not, I should have told you. I am going now to prepare a place for you, and after I have gone and prepared you a place, I shall return to take you with me; so that where I am you may be too. You know the way to the place where I am going.'

Thomas said, 'Lord, we do not know where you are going, so how can we know the way?' Jesus said:

'I am the Way, the Truth and the Life. No one can come to the Father except through me. If you know me, you know my Father too. From this moment you know him and have seen him.'

Philip said, 'Lord, let us see the Father and then we shall be satisfied.' 'Have I been with you all this time, Philip,' said Jesus to him 'and you still do not know me?

'To have seen me is to have seen the Father, so how can you say, "Let us see the Father"? Do you not believe that I am in the Father and the Father is in me? The words I say to you I do not speak as from myself: it is the Father, living in me, who is doing this work. You must believe me when I say that I am in the Father and the Father is in me; believe it on the evidence of this work, if for no other reason.

'I tell you most solemnly, whoever believes in me will perform the same works as I do myself, he will perform even greater works, because I am going to the Father.'

John 14:1-12

meditate

Everyone desires a place they can call home, whether it is modest or luxurious: a place to rest and relax. St Paul tells us our true home is heaven; it is there we will rest. All our life is preparation for that place of security and peace where God waits for us.

pray

God of power, look on me in my troubles and uncertainties; grant me serenity and a deep faith that my destiny is heaven. May I walk the right path and believe your truth so that from this moment onward I may experience the fulness of life.

act

All of us know people who are troubled, whose trust in life wavers. Take the chance to contact them and encourage them to put their confidence in God, who calls us to follow him.

MAY

£ 258

> *Without the Way there is no going; without the Truth there is no knowing; without the Life there is no living.*
>
> THOMAS À KEMPIS

14 SUN

Sainsburys with Ali

Bought DVD player

15 MON

16 TUES

ANVERGIA

MERTARIPINE INCREASED TO

30MG   BACK IN 8 WEEKS

GOT BIRTHDAY CARD FOR Jayne

17
WED

Jayne.

DIDN'T GO TO SEE MARIE COS
RUNNY NOSE. COLD ETC

18
THU

19
FRI

20
SAT

BUCKINGHAM Fionas grove
FLOWERS
BIRTHDAY CAKE 40 CANDLES.

read

SIXTH SUNDAY OF EASTER

Jesus said to his disciples:

'If you love me you will keep my commandments. I shall ask the Father, and he will give you another Advocate to be with you for ever, that Spirit of truth whom the world can never receive since it neither sees nor knows him, but you know him, because he is with you, he is in you. I will not leave you orphans; I will come back to you. In a short time the world will no longer see me; but you will see me, because I live and you will live. On that day you will understand that I am in my Father and you in me and I in you. Anybody who receives my commandments and keeps them will be one who loves me; and anybody who loves me will be loved by my Father, and I shall love him and show myself to him.'

John 14:15-21

meditate

The basis of our faith is that through baptism we are the children of God. He becomes our Father and therefore our identity is to be his sons and daughters. At times we might feel abandoned, orphaned. Jesus assures us of the coming of the spirit, bearing witness to our spirit that we are children and heirs of heaven.

pray

Almighty God, in your goodness you
have adopted us as your children;
send the Holy Spirit into our hearts so
that we may experience and indeed
behave as your children, trusting that
you are present to us always.

act

As Easter is drawing to its conclusion,
we are invited to ask for the gift of
the Holy Spirit. Join with others to ask
that spirit to come into your life.

MAY

As the soul is the life of the body, so the Holy Spirit is the life of our souls.

St Peter Damian

21
SUN

LITURGY OF THE HOURS DELIVERED.

22
MON

MEDS DELIVERED

To WILKO FOR BATTERY APPLE Man

23
TUES

FR JOHN CONFESSION & HOLY C

ANNE & IVOR Kings Highway

Sunday	Monday	Tuesday	Wednesday	Thursday (England & Wales)	Thursday (Scotland) ✠	Friday	Saturday ✠ (England)	Saturday (Wales & Scotland)
Acts 8:5-8, 14-17	Acts 16:11-15	Acts 16:22-34	Acts 17:15, 22 – 18:1	Acts 18:1-8	Acts 1:1-11	Acts 18:9-18	Acts 18:23-28	Acts 18:23-28
1 Peter 3:15-18	John 15:26	John 16:5-11	John 16:12-15	John 16:16-20	Ephesians 1:17-23	John 16:20-23	1 Thess 2:2-8	John 16:23-28
John 14:15-21	– 16:4				Matthew 28:16-20		Luke 10:1-9	

24
WED

HARVESTER WITH ALI
SKYPE MICHAEL

25
THU

DIVINE OFFICE VOLS ARRIVED

TO GAP & M.S FOR POLO SHIRTS &
TROUSERS
WALKED THERE AND BACK

✣ Ascension of the Lord (Scotland)

26
FRI

AM NOT WELL

27
SAT

✣ St Augustine of Canterbury, Bishop (England)

May | M T W T F S S M T W T F S S M T W T F S S M T W T F S S M T W
1 2 3 4 5 **6 7** 8 9 10 11 12 **13 14** 15 16 17 18 19 **20 21** 22 23 24 25 26 **27 28** 29 30 31

read

THE ASCENSION OF THE LORD

The eleven disciples set out for Galilee, to the mountain where Jesus had arranged to meet them. When they saw him they fell down before him, though some hesitated. Jesus came up and spoke to them. He said, 'All authority in heaven and on earth has been given to me. Go, therefore, make disciples of all the nations; baptise them in the name of the Father and of the Son and of the Holy Spirit, and teach them to observe all the commands I gave you. And know that I am with you always; yes, to the end of time.'

Matthew 28:16-20

meditate

When celebrating the Ascension of the Lord into heaven, we are not remembering a departure but, as the Gospel reminds us, we recall an ever presence. Jesus is Emmanuel – God with us, and he remains with us, always present in his body – the Church. This body continues to grow even today, and it does so through us.

pray

Ascended Lord, you sit at the right hand
of the Father and from there you will
come to judge the living and the dead.
Send down your spirit upon us, so that
your Church may grow, and many people
may come to know your love for them.

act

Jesus gives us the commission to
spread the Gospel by teaching others.
Try to speak with someone about your
Christian faith and how it helps you.

MAY

The facts are kind, and God is in the facts.

GERARD W. HUGHES

28
SUN

Ali WALK In Cewire Ilkeston
for Pre scription

✠ Ascension of the Lord (England, Wales and Ireland)

29
MON

Ali Called for A Cuppa

Her mum still in Hsp.

Bank Holiday (excluding Rep. of Ireland)

30
TUES

Sunday (England & Wales) ✠	Sunday (Scotland)	Monday	Tuesday	Wednesday ✠	Thursday	Friday	Saturday
Acts 1:1-11	Acts 1:12-14	Acts 19:1-8	Acts 20:17-27	Zephaniah 3:14-18	Acts 22:30;	Acts 25:13-21	Acts 28:16-20,
Ephesians 1:17-23	1 Peter 4:13-16	John 16:29-33	John 17:1-11	or Romans 12:9-16	23:6-11	John 21:15-19	30-31
Matthew 28:16-20	John 17:1-11			Luke 1:39-56	John 17:20-26		John 21:20-25

MAY – JUNE

31 WED

To M/z S

WALKED THERE & BACK
Ali's MUM HOME

✝ Visitation of the Blessed Virgin Mary

1 THU

To Sainsburys
walked there & back.

2 FRI

Ali DID SOME OF HER WORK
AND THEN TO Morrisons

3 SAT

1 WALKING Through The Vines
for Painting.

June

T F S S M T W T F S S M T W T F S S M T W T F S S M T W T F
1 2 3 4 5 6 7 8 9 10 11 12 13 14 15 16 17 18 19 20 21 22 23 24 25 26 27 28 29 30

read

PENTECOST

In the evening of the first day of the week, the doors were closed in the room where the disciples were, for fear of the Jews. Jesus came and stood among them. He said to them, 'Peace be with you,' and showed them his hands and his side. The disciples were filled with joy when they saw the Lord, and he said to them again, 'Peace be with you.

'As the Father sent me,
so am I sending you.'

After saying this he breathed on them and said:

'Receive the Holy Spirit.
For those whose sins you forgive,
they are forgiven;
for those whose sins you retain,
they are retained.'

John 20:19-23

meditate

Fear paralyses us and shuts us in. This is why the work of the Holy Spirit is to open doors, and lead us to spread the message of the Gospel. One of the ways we create barriers is by our sins, our judgements and our resentments. Therefore, the first task of those who receive the Spirit of God is to forgive and to reconcile.

pray

Come, Holy Spirit; dwell within us.
Purify me with your love so I may
accept God's forgiveness and be an
agent of reconciliation and peace.
May others know through me the
power of God's love and compassion.

act

St Francis prayed to be an instrument of
God's peace: bringing peace, reconciliation
and love to situations of hatred, discord and
misunderstanding. Are there any situations
that you could try to make better?

JUNE

4
SUN

Valking Thro the Viper delivered.

✣ Pentecost

5
MON

Bank Holiday (Rep. of Ireland)

6
TUES

Sunday ✣	Monday	Tuesday	Wednesday	Thursday	Friday (England & Wales)	Friday (Scotland) ✣	Saturday
Acts 2:1-11	Tobit 1:3; 2:1-8	Tobit 2:9-14	Tobit 3:1-11, 16-17	Tobit 6:10-11; 7:1, 9-14; 8:4-9	Tobit 11:5-17	Colossians 1:24-29	Tobit 12:1, 5-15, 20
1 Corinthians 12:3-7, 12-13	Mark 12:1-12	Mark 12:13-17	Mark 12:18-27	Mark 12:28-34	Mark 12:35-37	Mark 10:17-30	Mark 12:38-44
John 20:19-23							

7
WED

Jayne

[signature]

BATEMAN 87

8
THU

NAILS

9
FRI

Mod WALKED THERE AND BACK.

✠ St Columba (Scotland)

10
SAT

June

T	F	S	S	M	T	W	T	F	S	S	M	T	W	T	F	S	S	M	T	W	T	F	S	S	M	T	W	T	F
1	2	3	4	5	6	7	8	9	10	11	12	13	14	15	16	17	18	19	20	21	22	23	24	25	26	27	28	29	30

read

THE MOST HOLY TRINITY

Jesus said to Nicodemus:

'God loved the world so much that he gave his only Son, so that everyone who believes in him may not be lost but may have eternal life. For God sent his Son into the world not to condemn the world, but so that through him the world might be saved. No one who believes in him will be condemned; but whoever refuses to believe is condemned already, because he has refused to believe in the name of God's only Son.

John 3:16-18

meditate

We believe that God will judge us, but at the same time we profess that he is merciful. What will his judgement consist of? The verdict is love and the judgement is whether or not we accept this love, which is free and total. Condemnation is possible only if we refuse to accept this forgiveness.

pray

God of love, you created us for yourself
and in Jesus your Son reclaimed us as your
possession. Send the Holy Spirit to dwell
in me, so I may accept your care for me.

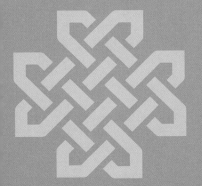

act

One of the ways in which we accept
God's love is by going to confession.
Consider whether or not you might
benefit from celebrating this sacrament.

JUNE

You know well enough that Our Lord does not look so much at the greatness of our actions, nor even at their difficulty, but at the love with which we do them.

St Thérèse of Lisieux

11
~~SUN~~
TUE

FINISHED SERIES / SOPRANOS
GAS SAFETY CHECK
SAINSBURYS WITH ALI
DOCTOR CHANGED STATINS AND OINTMENT.
PEAR TREE NOW MY CHEMISTS

✠ The Most Holy Trinity

12
MON

GAS SAFETY CHECK
SAINSBURYS WITH ALI
DOCTOR CHANGED STATINS AND OINTMENT
PEAR TREE PHARMACY NOW MY CHEMIST

13
TUES

STARTED Ointment for legs

Sunday ✠
Exodus 34:4-6, 8-9
2 Corinthians 13:11-13
John 3:16-18

Monday
2 Corinthians 1:1-7
Matthew 5:1-12

Tuesday
2 Corinthians 1:18-22
Matthew 5:13-16

Wednesday
2 Corinthians 3:4-11
Matthew 5:17-19

Thursday
2 Corinthians 3:15
– 4:1, 3-6
Matthew 5:20-26

Friday
2 Corinthians 4:7-15
Matthew 5:27-32

Saturday
2 Corinthians 5:14-21
Matthew 5:33-37

14
WED

M & S.

WALKED THERE AND BACK.

15
THU

BLISTER PACKS

~~M & S BLISTER PACKS~~ DELIVERED.

BOOKS TO LIBRARY

HAIR CUT

16
FRI

WALKED 20 MINS

17
SAT

June

T F S S M T W T F S S M T W T F S S M T W T F S S M T W T F
1 2 3 4 5 6 7 8 9 10 11 12 13 14 15 16 17 18 19 20 21 22 23 24 25 26 27 28 29 30

read

THE MOST HOLY BODY AND BLOOD OF CHRIST (CORPUS CHRISTI)

Jesus said to the Jews:

'I am the living bread which has come down from heaven. Anyone who eats this bread will live for ever; and the bread that I shall give is my flesh, for the life of the world.'

Then the Jews started arguing with one another: 'How can this man give us his flesh to eat?' they said. Jesus replied:

'I tell you most solemnly, if you do not eat the flesh of the Son of Man and drink his blood, you will not have life in you. Anyone who does eat my flesh and drink my blood has eternal life, and I shall raise him up on the last day. For my flesh is real food and my blood is real drink. He who eats my flesh and drinks my blood lives in me and I live in him. As I, who am sent by the living Father, myself draw life from the Father, so whoever eats me will draw life from me. This is the bread come down from heaven, not like the bread our ancestors ate: they are dead, but anyone who eats this bread will live for ever.'

John 6:51-58

meditate

"As I draw life from the Father who sent me, so whoever eats me will draw life from me". The question today is, where do we draw life from? If upon sincere reflection our source of energy is not God, we would do well to change direction and turn to him.

pray

Lord of life, you want to meet us in our every need. Come to me and satisfy my desires. May I draw strength and courage from you, so I may share your joy with others.

act

Drawing life from God in the Eucharistic Christ means not only receiving him in Holy Communion, but also adoring him in the Blessed Sacrament. You might try to find some time to spend in prayer before Holy Communion, drawing life from Jesus.

JUNE

If angels could be jealous of men, they would be so for one reason: Holy Communion.

St Maximilian Kolbe

18
SUN

Maz came with Wrapped a Bagle Good.

Swapped Mac for new laptop

✣ The Most Holy Body and Blood of Christ (Corpus Christi); Father's Day

19
MON

Sainsburys with Ali

20
TUES

Sunday ✣	Monday	Tuesday	Wednesday	Thursday (England) ✣	Thursday (Wales & Scotland)	Friday ✣	Saturday ✣
Deut 8:2-3, 14-16	2 Cor 6:1-10	2 Cor 8:1-9	2 Cor 9:6-11	2 Maccabees 6:18, 21, 24-31	2 Cor 11:1-11	Deut 7:6-11	Isaiah 49:1-6
1 Cor 10:16-17	Matthew 5:38-42	Matthew 5:43-48	Matthew 6:1-6, 16-18	Matthew 24:4-13	Matthew 6:7-15	1 John 4:7-16	Acts 13:22-26
John 6:51-58						Matthew 11:25-30	Luke 1:57-66, 80

21
WED

22
THU

Black Cartridge.

✠ SS John Fisher and Thomas More (England)

23
FRI

✠ The Most Sacred Heart of Jesus

24
SAT

✠ The Nativity of St John the Baptist

June	T	F	S	S	M	T	W	T	F	S	S	M	T	W	T	F	S	S	M	T	W	T	F	S	S	M	T	W	T	F
	1	2	3	4	5	6	7	8	9	10	11	12	13	14	15	16	17	18	19	20	21	22	23	24	25	26	27	28	29	30

read

Jesus instructed the Twelve as follows: 'Do not be afraid. For everything that is now covered will be uncovered, and everything now hidden will be made clear. What I say to you in the dark, tell in the daylight; what you hear in whispers, proclaim from the house-tops.

'Do not be afraid of those who kill the body but cannot kill the soul; fear him rather who can destroy both body and soul in hell. Can you not buy two sparrows for a penny? And yet not one falls to the ground without your Father knowing. Why, every hair on your head has been counted. So there is no need to be afraid; you are worth more than hundreds of sparrows.

'So if anyone declares himself for me in the presence of men, I will declare myself for him in the presence of my Father in heaven. But the one who disowns me in the presence of men, I will disown in the presence of my Father in heaven.'

Matthew 10:26-33

meditate

Christianity is a public religion, and an integral part of our belief is sharing it with others. All sorts of things prevent us from communicating the joy of our faith. Fear is the main one. Perhaps not so much physical fear as fear of what people will think or say about us. Jesus will be with us when we bear witness to him.

pray

Ever-present God, come to my aid so
that I may let others know that I am your
disciple. Conquer fear in my life and give
me the strength to declare myself for
you in the presence of everyone.

act

With the courage that this reading
gives, you might want to speak to
others about what you do on Sundays
when you go to Church, and perhaps
even say why you do it.

JUNE

*Reflect upon your present blessings, of which every man has many;
not on your past misfortunes, of which all men have some.*

CHARLES DICKENS

25 SUN

Phone call asking for prayer
New laptop

26 MON

Sainsburys with Ali

27 TUES

OUT PATIENTS 9.30

HOLLAND & BARRET MULTI VITAMINS

Sunday
Jeremiah 20:10-13
Romans 5:12-15
Matthew 10:26-33

Monday
Genesis 12:1-9
Matthew 7:1-5

Tuesday
Genesis 13:2, 5-18
Matthew 7:6, 12-14

Wednesday
Genesis 15:1-12,
17-18
Matthew 7:15-20

Thursday ✝
Acts 12:1-11
2 Timothy 4:6-8, 17-18
Matthew 16:13-19

Friday
Genesis 17:1, 9-10,
15-22
Matthew 8:1-4

Saturday
Genesis 18:1-15
Matthew 8:5-17

28 WED

Windows 8.1 DOWNLOAD
PROBLEM

29 THU

5.30 WINDOWS PROBLEM PHONE CALL

✣ SS Peter and Paul, Apostles

30 FRI

P. to World for Flash Drive

Morrisons with Ali

1 SAT

July

S S M T W T F S S M T W T F S S M T W T F S S M T W T F S S M
1 2 3 4 5 6 7 8 9 10 11 12 13 14 15 16 17 18 19 20 21 22 23 24 25 26 27 28 29 30 31

read

Jesus instructed the Twelve as follows: 'Anyone who prefers father or mother to me is not worthy of me. Anyone who prefers son or daughter to me is not worthy of me. Anyone who does not take his cross and follow in my footsteps is not worthy of me. Anyone who finds his life will lose it; anyone who loses his life for my sake will find it.

'Anyone who welcomes you welcomes me; and those who welcome me welcome the one who sent me.

'Anyone who welcomes a prophet because he is a prophet will have a prophet's reward; and anyone who welcomes a holy man because he is a holy man will have a holy man's reward.

'If anyone gives so much as a cup of cold water to one of these little ones because he is a disciple, then I tell you solemnly, he will most certainly not lose his reward.'

Matthew 10:37-42

meditate

Jesus loves us totally and requires us to love him in the same manner. That is, radically and totally. If he is at the centre of our love and desire, our concern for ourselves and for everybody else will fall into its right place.

pray

Lord Jesus, you invite us to follow in your
footsteps; give me the courage to love you
above all things so that all other aspects
of my life may fall into their right place.

act

Jesus invites us to see him present in
other people, welcoming them or giving
them something to drink. Perhaps you
could try practising one of these works
of mercy towards others.

JULY

Love, Hope, and Reverence are realities of a different order from the senses, but they are positive and constant facts, always active, always working out mighty changes in human life.

ELIZABETH BLACKWELL

2
SUN

RATE THE RACES SPEED RATINGS SOFTWARE

3
MON

Windows 8.1 Download.

Twins (20) 1997

✣ St Thomas, Apostle

4
TUES

Birthday Cards for Twins Posted

5
WED

Jayné

Windows 10 up & running

Some changes now O.K.

6
THU

7
FRI

Marié & Pat

Ali Sainsbury

Holy Communion

8
SAT

July

S S M T W T F S S M T W T F S S M T W T F S S M T W T F S S M
1 2 3 4 5 6 7 8 9 10 11 12 13 14 15 16 17 18 19 20 21 22 23 24 25 26 27 28 29 30 31

read

FOURTEENTH SUNDAY IN ORDINARY TIME

Jesus exclaimed, 'I bless you, Father, Lord of heaven and of earth, for hiding these things from the learned and the clever and revealing them to mere children. Yes, Father, for that is what it pleased you to do. Everything has been entrusted to me by my Father; and no one knows the Son except the Father, just as no one knows the Father except the Son and those to whom the Son chooses to reveal him.

'Come to me, all you who labour and are overburdened, and I will give you rest. Shoulder my yoke and learn from me, for I am gentle and humble in heart, and you will find rest for your souls. Yes, my yoke is easy and my burden light.'

Matthew 11:25-30

meditate

Christianity belongs to those who are small – to the children. Jesus reminds us more than once that unless we become like little children we will never enter the kingdom of heaven. A child is open to learning new things and experiencing old things anew. Therefore, we are invited to give up the ways we have learnt, and to be surprised by God.

pray

Lord Jesus Christ, you are meek and humble of heart; transform my heart to be like you; renew my life so that in simplicity I may accept the burdens you impose on me, knowing that you carry them with me.

act

With Jesus the burdens we carry are easy and light. At times we are called to help others carry their load. You might consider doing this with someone around you.

JULY

Faith is not a light which scatters all our darkness, but a lamp which guides our steps in the night and suffices for the journey.

POPE FRANCIS

9
SUN

10
MON

ALL HAD POWER NAP.

11
TUES

DVD PRAYER ARRIVED.

✠ St Benedict, Abbot

Sunday	Monday	Tuesday ✠	Wednesday	Thursday	Friday	Saturday
Zechariah 9:9-10	Genesis 28:10-22	Proverbs 2:1-9	Genesis 41:55-57;	Genesis 44:18-21,	Genesis 46:1-7, 28-30	Genesis 49:29-33;
Romans 8:9, 11-13	Matthew 9:18-26	Matthew 19:27-29	42:5-7, 17-24	23-29; 45:1-5	Matthew 10:16-23	50:15-26
Matthew 11:25-30			Matthew 10:1-7	Matthew 10:7-15		Matthew 10:24-38

12 WED

DRI BLOOD TEST

ARRANGED SURVEY FOR CENTRAL HEATING 1st AUG

Bank Holiday (N. Ireland)

13 THU

TOE NAILS

M&S.

14 FRI

B

BATEMAN ST WALK

15 SAT

July	S	S	M	T	W	T	F	S	S	M	T	W	T	F	S	S	M	T	W	T	F	S	S	M	T	W	T	F	S	S	M
	1	2	3	4	5	6	7	8	9	10	11	12	13	14	15	16	17	18	19	20	21	22	23	24	25	26	27	28	29	30	31

read

FIFTEENTH SUNDAY IN ORDINARY TIME

Jesus left the house and sat by the lakeside, but such crowds gathered round him that he got into a boat and sat there. The people all stood on the beach, and he told them many things in parables.

He said, 'Imagine a sower going out to sow. As he sowed, some seeds fell on the edge of the path, and the birds came and ate them up. Others fell on patches of rock where they found little soil and sprang up straight away, because there was no depth of earth; but as soon as the sun came up they were scorched and, not having any roots, they withered away. Others fell among thorns, and the thorns grew up and choked them. Others fell on rich soil and produced their crop, some a hundredfold, some sixty, some thirty. Listen, anyone who has ears!'

Matthew 13:1-9
(Longer form *Matthew* 13:1-23)

meditate

The sower goes out to do his work and is generous with the seed. He does not discriminate against types of soil which might not produce the desired crop. The fields have been prepared by someone else. What kind of soil are we? Has the preparation happened?

pray

God and master of the harvest, you see
my heart and know the times when my
life is not ready to receive you. Soften
the hardness of my heart; take away the
stones and the thorns so that I may be
the good soil where Jesus can grow.

act

Consider what kind of soil you are,
as well as what might be needed
to become the good soil we were
created to be.

JULY

Don't judge each day by the harvest you reap, but by the seeds you plant.

ATTRIBUTED TO ROBERT LOUIS STEVENSON

16
SUN

TRAIN STATION CASH & PAPER.

17
MON

SAINSBURYS with Ali

18
TUES

LONDON ROAD — BRADSHAW WAY

PAID ____ Lady.

Sunday	Monday	Tuesday	Wednesday	Thursday	Friday	Saturday ✣
Isaiah 55:10-11	Exodus 1:8-14, 22	Exodus 2:1-15	Exodus 3:1-6, 9-12	Exodus 3:13-20	Exodus 11:10 –12:14	Song of Songs 3:1-4 or
Romans 8:18-23	Matthew 10:34 – 11:1	Matthew 11:20-24	Matthew 11:25-27	Matthew 11:28-30	Matthew 12:1-8	2 Corinthians 5:14-17
Matthew 13:1-23						John 20:1-2, 11-18

19
WED

Jayné.

20
THU

Ahl BALLET AT BIRMINGHAY.

21
FRI

SAINSBURYS BY BUS
WALKED BACK
CHAT WITH STEDHEN ON PHONE

22
SAT

✝ St Mary Magdalene

July

	S	S	M	T	W	T	F	S	S	M	T	W	T	F	S	S	M	T	W	T	F	S	S	M	T	W	T	F	S	S	M
	1	2	3	4	5	6	7	8	9	10	11	12	13	14	15	16	17	18	19	20	21	22	23	24	25	26	27	28	29	30	31

read

SIXTEENTH SUNDAY IN ORDINARY TIME

Jesus put another parable before the crowds: 'The kingdom of heaven may be compared to a man who sowed good seed in his field. While everybody was asleep his enemy came, sowed darnel all among the wheat, and made off. When the new wheat sprouted and ripened, the darnel appeared as well. The owner's servants went to him and said, "Sir, was it not good seed that you sowed in your field? If so, where does the darnel come from?" "Some enemy has done this" he answered. And the servants said, "Do you want us to go and weed it out?" But he said, "No, because when you weed out the darnel you might pull up the wheat with it. Let them both grow till the harvest; and at harvest time I shall say to the reapers: First collect the darnel and tie it in bundles to be burnt, then gather the wheat into my barn."'

Matthew 13:24-30
(Longer form *Matthew* 13:24-43)

meditate

When we look at our lives there are patches of good seed and others of darnel. Both plants look alike at first; only with time can they be told apart. A wise farmer waits patiently until they are grown; only then does he intervene. This is how he preserves the good seed.

pray

Lord of wisdom, give me patience to
see the development in my life; grant
me discernment to look at my life and
discover what needs to be uprooted.
Then I will be able to produce the fruit
for which you created me.

act

Darnel produces a fruit which can be
poisonous. Take a moment to consider
your words and actions, and see whether
the time has come to try and stop those
which are not healthy.

JULY

God could complain about us a great deal more than we about him. We complain that he does not make himself present to us for the few minutes we reserve for him, but what about the twenty-three and a half hours during which God may be knocking at our door and we answer 'I am busy, I am sorry'?

METROPOLITAN ANTHONY OF SOUROZH

23
SUN

STATION Sunday Fete Independent

24
MON

SAINSBURYS Ali

25
TUES

POSTED VOTER REG. Fory.

✠ St James, Apostle

Sunday	Monday	Tuesday ✠	Wednesday	Thursday	Friday	Saturday
Wisdom 12:13, 16-19	Exodus 14:5-18	2 Corinthians 4:7-15	Exodus 16:1-5, 9-15	Exodus 19:1-2, 9-11, 16-20	Exodus 20:1-17	Exodus 24:3-8
Romans 8:26-27	Matthew 12:38-42	Matthew 20:20-28	Matthew 13:1-9	Matthew 13:10-17	Matthew 13:18-23	Matthew 13:24-30
Matthew 13:24-43						

JULY

26 WED

ALL TO U.S.A.

27 THU

BATEMAN ST WALK.

28 FRI

29 SAT

SKY SPORTS
GAELIC FOOTBALL

July | S S M T W T F S S M T W T F S S M T W T F S S M T W T F S S M
1 2 3 4 5 6 7 8 9 10 11 12 13 14 15 16 17 18 19 20 21 22 23 24 25 26 27 28 29 30 31

read

SEVENTEENTH SUNDAY IN ORDINARY TIME

Jesus said to the crowds: 'The kingdom of heaven is like treasure hidden in a field which someone has found; he hides it again, goes off happy, sells everything he owns and buys the field.

'Again, the kingdom of heaven is like a merchant looking for fine pearls; when he finds one of great value he goes and sells everything he owns and buys it.

'Again, the kingdom of heaven is like a dragnet cast into the sea that brings in a haul of all kinds. When it is full, the fishermen haul it ashore; then, sitting down, they collect the good ones in a basket and throw away those that are no use. This is how it will be at the end of time: the angels will appear and separate the wicked from the just to throw them into the blazing furnace where there will be weeping and grinding of teeth.

'Have you understood all this?' They said, 'Yes.' And he said to them, 'Well then, every scribe who becomes a disciple of the kingdom of heaven is like a householder who brings out from his storeroom things both new and old.'

Matthew 13:44-52

meditate

The Kingdom of God belongs to those who actively look for it, and to those who find it by chance. Both resolve to give up everything for the kingdom, in the knowledge that "to give all the goods of one's house for this love would be to despise it" (Sg 8:7).

pray

Lord of all graciousness, you promise us a hundredfold anything we give for your sake; grant me the spirit of abundance so that I may give without counting the cost, with my eyes constantly fixed on the reward you promise.

act

God calls us to put our whole trust in him. This includes our money and possessions. This is the time in which you might take a risk and give up some of these for him, so you may experience his reward.

JULY – AUGUST

No one has ever become poor from giving.

ANNE FRANK

30
SUN

3ʳᵈ Anniv Admit to Hosp for Stroke 2014
Station Money
Mr Booze Sun Times & Tiler

31
MON

M&S
WALKED BAC
Dr Norman 8.20
for
RANITIDINE Prescription
WALKED BACK.

1
TUES

11.00AY Survey for Central Heating
new Boiler.

Sunday	Monday	Tuesday	Wednesday	Thursday	Friday	Saturday
1 Kings 3:5, 7-12	Exodus 32:15-24,	Exodus 33:7-11;	Exodus 34:29-35	Exodus 40:16-21,	Leviticus 23:1, 4-11,	Leviticus 25:1, 8-17
Romans 8:28-30	30-34	34:5-9, 28	Matthew 13:44-46	34-38	15-16, 27, 34-37	Matthew 14:1-12
Matthew 13:44-52	Matthew 13:31-35	Matthew 13:36-43		Matthew 13:47-53	Matthew 13:54-58	

2 WED

2014 STROKE OP.

TAXI TO
CHIROPRACTOR ANDY OLIVER 1.45.
GOOD SESSION — WILL HAVE 6 MORE

3 THU

2014 STROKE ~~OPERATION~~.

SAINSBURYS
WALKED BACK.

4 FRI

WALK BATEMAN ST.

5 SAT

M.S.
WALKING

read

THE TRANSFIGURATION OF THE LORD

Jesus took with him Peter and James and his brother John and led them up a high mountain where they could be alone. There in their presence he was transfigured: his face shone like the sun and his clothes became as white as the light. Suddenly Moses and Elijah appeared to them; they were talking with him. Then Peter spoke to Jesus. 'Lord,' he said 'it is wonderful for us to be here; if you wish, I will make three tents here, one for you, one for Moses and one for Elijah.' He was still speaking when suddenly a bright cloud covered them with shadow, and from the cloud there came a voice which said, 'This is my Son, the Beloved; he enjoys my favour. Listen to him.' When they heard this, the disciples fell on their faces, overcome with fear. But Jesus came up and touched them. 'Stand up,' he said 'do not be afraid.' And when they raised their eyes they saw no one but only Jesus.

As they came down from the mountain Jesus gave them this order, 'Tell no one about the vision until the Son of Man has risen from the dead.'

Matthew 17:1-9

meditate

"This is my Son, the Beloved; he enjoys my favour. Listen to him!"
In the middle of the summer, when we might be on holiday, the invitation comes to listen to Jesus. Listening to Christ is imitating his example of service, and his example of spending time with others – for others.

pray

Lord Jesus, on the mountain you were transfigured, showing us the way to the Father. Open my eyes to your presence and my ears to listen to you in the voice of my brothers and sisters.

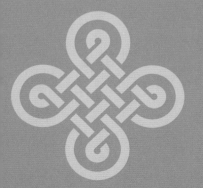

act

"Listen!" is the invitation of this Sunday. You might try to make some extra time for silence and prayer, to hear what God wants you to do.

AUGUST

> I learned that courage was not the absence of fear, but the
> triumph over it. The brave man is not he who does not feel
> afraid, but he who conquers that fear.
>
> NELSON MANDELA

6
SUN

E MAIL FROM ALL
ALL GONE WELL WITH HOLIDAY.

✛ Transfiguration of the Lord

7
MON

LISTER HOUSE TO ORDER
COPY OF MEDICAL RECORDS
HOSP SINCE JAN 2000

Bank Holiday (Scotland and Rep. of Ireland)

8
TUES

CENTRAL HEATING SURVEY 11.00AM

Sunday ✛	Monday	Tuesday	Wednesday ✛	Thursday ✛	Friday	Saturday
Daniel 7:9-10, 13-14	Numbers 11:4-15	Numbers 12:1-13	Hosea 2:16-17, 21-22	2 Corinthians 9:6-10	Deuteronomy	Deuteronomy 6:4-13
2 Peter 1:16-19	Matthew 14:13-21	Matthew 14:22-36	Matthew 25:1-13	John 12:24-26	4:32-40	Matthew 17:14-20
Matthew 17:1-9					Matthew 16:24-28	

9
WED

MARIE RANG SHE'S ABIT BETTER

3 45 CHIROPRACTOR TAXI

WALKED TO TOWN

B' CARD FOR WILLIAM

SAINSBURYS

✣ St Teresa Benedicta of the Cross, Virgin and Martyr

10
THU

✣ St Lawrence, Deacon and Martyr

11
FRI

A. MAY R.I.P 1981

WILLIAMS BIRTHDAY 2000

MEDICINES DELIVERED.

ALI'S MUM DRI — ~~TRANSFER~~

BEING TRANSFERRED

BACK TO ROYAL

PRAYER SHARE WORD CHAT

THS for Good.

12
SAT

August	T	W	T	F	S	S	M	T	W	T	F	S	S	M	T	W	T	F	S	S	M	T	W	T	F	S	S	M	T	W	T
	1	2	3	4	5	6	7	8	9	10	11	12	13	14	15	16	17	18	19	20	21	22	23	24	25	26	27	28	29	30	31

read

NINETEENTH SUNDAY IN ORDINARY TIME

Jesus made the disciples get into the boat and go on ahead to the other side while he would send the crowds away. After sending the crowds away he went up into the hills by himself to pray. When evening came, he was there alone, while the boat, by now far out on the lake, was battling with a heavy sea, for there was a headwind. In the fourth watch of the night he went towards them, walking on the lake, and when the disciples saw him walking on the lake they were terrified. 'It is a ghost' they said, and cried out in fear. But at once Jesus called out to them, saying, 'Courage! It is I! Do not be afraid.' It was Peter who answered. 'Lord,' he said 'if it is you, tell me to come to you across the water.' 'Come' said Jesus. Then Peter got out of the boat and started walking towards Jesus across the water, but as soon as he felt the force of the wind, he took fright and began to sink. 'Lord! Save me!' he cried. Jesus put out his hand at once and held him. 'Man of little faith,' he said 'why did you doubt?' And as they got into the boat the wind dropped. The men in the boat bowed down before him and said, 'Truly, you are the Son of God.'

Matthew 14:22-33

meditate

Jesus knew the sea and how rough it might become. All the same, he sent his disciples ahead of him into the storm. After they had been battling for a while, he encouraged them by saying: "Do not be afraid! It is I!" In the storms of life, Jesus comes to meet us: wait for him!

pray

Lord Jesus, you do not abandon us in our troubles and sufferings; grant me the eyes to see you coming and the faith to call on you so I may arrive safely at my final destination.

act

All of us go through rough moments in life and, like the apostles, we are not alone. Consider how you can help those in difficulties or think about whom you could call if you are going through a difficult moment.

AUGUST

We shall steer safely through every storm, so long as our heart is right, our intention fervent, our courage steadfast, and our trust fixed on God.

ST FRANCIS DE SALES

13
SUN

14
MON

Sainsbury's

Walk Back

15
TUES

Station for Cash

Mr Booze Milk + Vegetable

Sunday	Monday	Tuesday ✢	Wednesday	Thursday	Friday	Saturday
1 Kings 19:9, 11-13	Deuteronomy 10:12-22	Revelation 11:19; 12:1-6, 10	Deuteronomy 34:1-12	Joshua 3:7-11, 13-17	Joshua 24:1-13	Joshua 24:14-29
Romans 9:1-5		1 Corinthians 15:20-26		Matthew 18:21 – 19:1	Matthew 19:3-12	Matthew 19:13-15
Matthew 14:22-33	Matthew 17:22-27	Luke 1:39-56	Matthew 18:15-20			

16 WED

CHIROPRACTOR 2.00

TAXI TO CHIROPRACTOR 2.00

WALK BACK VIA M.S.

17 THU

POSTED CLAIM FORM TO ABBEY LIFE £1436

HAIRCUT SAINSBURYS BUS.

18 FRI

ALI HOME TODAY

BATEMAN ST O

19 SAT

ALL HOME TODAY.

MR BOOZE FOR MILK

August

T W T F S S M T W T F S S M T W T F S S M T W T F S S M T W T
1 2 3 4 5 6 7 8 9 10 11 12 13 14 15 16 17 18 19 20 21 22 23 24 25 26 27 28 29 30 31

read

TWENTIETH SUNDAY IN ORDINARY TIME

Jesus left Gennesaret and withdrew to the region of Tyre and Sidon. Then out came a Canaanite woman from that district and started shouting, 'Sir, Son of David, take pity on me. My daughter is tormented by a devil.' But he answered her not a word. And his disciples went and pleaded with him. 'Give her what she wants,' they said 'because she is shouting after us.' He said in reply, 'I was sent only to the lost sheep of the House of Israel.' But the woman had come up and was kneeling at his feet. 'Lord,' she said 'help me.' He replied, 'It is not fair to take the children's food and throw it to the house-dogs.' She retorted, 'Ah yes, sir; but even house-dogs can eat the scraps that fall from their master's table.' Then Jesus answered her, 'Woman, you have great faith. Let your wish be granted.' And from that moment her daughter was well again.

Matthew 15:21-28

meditate

What is the first step of prayer? Today's Gospel gives us an answer: humility. The woman comes with an urgent request. But before an apparent refusal, she accepts she does not deserve anything. Then Jesus grants her desire. Nothing attracts God more than a humble spirit.

pray

Lord Jesus, healer of body and soul,
you care for the good of all people.
Grant me the humility to accept my life.

act

Moved by care and concern for her
daughter, this woman interceded
for her. Perhaps there is someone
who needs your prayers.

AUGUST

As the sun never stops shining – though we cannot always see its rays – so God is always shedding his graces and his healing powers on each of us.

ATTRIBUTED TO FULTON J. SHEEN

20 SUN

KERRY MAYO DRAW AT CROKE PARK.

21 MON

2.40
TELEPHONE APPT PSA RESULT
SAINSBURYS WITH ALI

22 TUES

BED DELIVERED TO ALI'S MUM.
ALI'S MUM HOME
STATION FOR CASH.

Sunday	Monday	Tuesday	Wednesday	Thursday ✠	Friday	Saturday
Isaiah 56:1, 6-7	Judges 2:11-19	Judges 6:11-24	Judges 9:6-15	Revelation 21:9-14	Ruth 1:1, 3-6,	Ruth 2:1-3, 8-11;
Romans 11:13-15, 29-32	Matthew 19:16-22	Matthew 19:23-30	Matthew 20:1-16	John 1:45-51	14-16, 22	4:13-17
Matthew 15:21-28					Matthew 22:34-40	Matthew 23:1-12

23 WED

TAXI TO CHIROPRACTOR

WALK TO TOWN BUS HOME.

24 THU

✠ St Bartholomew, Apostle

25 FRI

WALK BATEMAN ST.

26 SAT

BUS TO T. S

WALK BACK.

MAYO BEAT KERRY.

read

When Jesus came to the region of Caesarea Philippi he put this question to his disciples, 'Who do people say the Son of Man is?' And they said, 'Some say he is John the Baptist, some Elijah, and others Jeremiah or one of the prophets.' 'But you,' he said, 'who do you say I am?' Then Simon Peter spoke up, 'You are the Christ,' he said 'the Son of the living God.' Jesus replied, 'Simon son of Jonah, you are a happy man! Because it was not flesh and blood that revealed this to you but my Father in heaven. So I now say to you: You are Peter and on this rock I will build my Church. And the gates of the underworld can never hold out against it. I will give you the keys of the kingdom of heaven: whatever you bind on earth shall be considered bound in heaven; whatever you loose on earth shall be considered loosed in heaven.' Then he gave the disciples strict orders not to tell anyone that he was the Christ.

Matthew 16:13-20

meditate

There is a moment in which we need to ask ourselves, "Who is Jesus for me?" People around us have their own answers, but every follower of Jesus needs to wrestle with this question. The faith of the apostles shows us the way, but ultimately we have to make it personal.

pray

God our Father, show me the way,
the path to follow so that I may
profess with my lips and lead my
life by the faith which, together
with the whole church, I share.

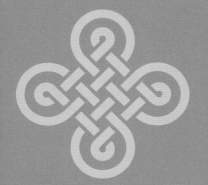

act

During this week, try to pray and
understand better what it means for
Jesus to be the Messiah, the Son of
the living God.

AUGUST

Nothing would be done at all if a man waited till he could do it so well, that no one could find fault with it.

JOHN HENRY NEWMAN

27
SUN

STATION FOR INDEPENDANT Ireland

28
MON

MARIE P.M. WITH ALI.
M. S.

Bank Holiday (except Scotland and Rep. of Ireland)

29
TUES

Sunday	Monday	Tuesday	Wednesday	Thursday	Friday	Saturday
Isaiah 22:19-23	1 Thessalonians	1 Thessalonians 2:1-8	1 Thessalonians 2:9-13	1 Thessalonians	1 Thessalonians 4:1-8	1 Thessalonians 4:9-11
Romans 11:33-36	1:1-5, 8-10	Matthew 23:23-26	Matthew 23:27-32	3:7-13	Matthew 25:1-13	Matthew 25:14-30
Matthew 16:13-20	Matthew 23:13-22			Matthew 24:42-51		

30
WED

MARIÉ WITH ALI

31
THU

1
FRI

HOLY COMMUNION ST JOSEPH'S
ALI SAINSBURY'S

2
SAT

SKYPÉ ANNE & IVOR.

September	F	S	S	M	T	W	T	F	S	S	M	T	W	T	F	S	S	M	T	W	T	F	S	S	M	T	W	T	F	S
	1	2	3	4	5	6	7	8	9	10	11	12	13	14	15	16	17	18	19	20	21	22	23	24	25	26	27	28	29	30

read

Jesus began to make it clear to his disciples that he was destined to go to Jerusalem and suffer grievously at the hands of the elders and chief priests and scribes, to be put to death and to be raised up on the third day. Then, taking him aside, Peter started to remonstrate with him. 'Heaven preserve you, Lord,' he said. 'This must not happen to you.' But he turned and said to Peter, 'Get behind me, Satan! You are an obstacle in my path, because the way you think is not God's way but man's.'

Then Jesus said to his disciples, 'If anyone wants to be a follower of mine, let him renounce himself and take up his cross and follow me. For anyone who wants to save his life will lose it; but anyone who loses his life for my sake will find it. What, then, will a man gain if he wins the whole world and ruins his life? Or what has a man to offer in exchange for his life?

'For the Son of Man is going to come in the glory of his Father with his angels, and, when he does, he will reward each one according to his behaviour.'

Matthew 16:21-27

meditate

Because we love and care about people, we do not want them to suffer. This is Peter's main concern. In Jesus, though, we see a new meaning to our suffering and death. They do not have the final word; hence Jesus invites his disciples to follow in his footsteps by taking up their personal cross.

pray

Lord Jesus, you mounted the wood of the cross because you love us. Send me the Holy Spirit so I may understand that, through my everyday cross, I can be like you, losing my life so as to receive it back from you.

act

When Jesus took up his own cross, different people helped him: Simon of Cyrene, Veronica. Reflect on how you could help others carry their own cross.

SEPTEMBER

If you aren't in over your head, how do you know how tall you are?

T. S. ELIOT

3
SUN

STATION FOR SUNDAY INDEPENDENT

GALWAY BEAT WATERFORD ALL IRELAND.

4
MON

ARBORETUM. WALK

5
TUES

SKYPE MICHAEL.

6
WED

C.

CHIROPRACTOR 2.00 TAXI

BUS BACK.

7
THU

SAINSBURYS WITH ALI

CARTRIDGES FOR PRINTER.

8
FRI

BANK TO DEPOSIT CHEQUE #1436
ABBEY LIFE.

✠ The Nativity of the Blessed Virgin Mary

9
SAT

September

F S S M T W T F S S M T W T F S S M T W T F S S M T W T F S
1 2 3 4 5 6 7 8 9 10 11 12 13 14 15 16 17 18 19 20 21 22 23 24 25 26 27 28 29 30

read

TWENTY-THIRD SUNDAY IN ORDINARY TIME

Jesus said to his disciples: 'If your brother does something wrong, go and have it out with him alone, between your two selves. If he listens to you, you have won back your brother. If he does not listen, take one or two others along with you: the evidence of two or three witnesses is required to sustain any charge. But if he refuses to listen to these, report it to the community; and if he refuses to listen to the community, treat him like a pagan or a tax collector.

'I tell you solemnly, whatever you bind on earth shall be considered bound in heaven; whatever you loose on earth shall be considered loosed in heaven.

'I tell you solemnly once again, if two of you on earth agree to ask anything at all, it will be granted to you by my Father in heaven. For where two or three meet in my name, I shall be there with them.'

Matthew 18:15-20

meditate

One of the spiritual works of mercy is admonishing sinners. This may seem simple but it is actually very difficult. We should correct those who do wrong not out of moralism or to patronise them, but because we love them. We are part of the same body and their fall is our fall, too.

Father, grant me discernment to
understand how I can best help my brother
or sister; to know the right moment and
the right words to use. Give me courage
to admonish them and humility to accept
their reaction.

act

The Gospel gives a clear procedure about
how to deal with those we see doing
wrong. Perhaps the time has come to speak
to someone who might benefit from a word
of warning or positive encouragement.

SEPTEMBER

No man is an island, entire of itself; every man is a piece of the continent, a part of the main.

JOHN DONNE

10
SUN

Sunday Independent Train Station

11
MON

MEDICINES DELIVERED.

12
TUES

1/2 S. Bus
WALK BACK.

Sunday
Ezekiel 33:7-9
Romans 13:8-10
Matthew 18:15-20

Monday
Colossians 1:24 – 2:3
Luke 6:6-11

Tuesday
Colossians 2:6-15
Luke 6:12-19

Wednesday
Colossians 3:1-11
Luke 6:20-26

Thursday ✣
Numbers 21:4-9
Philippians 2:6-11
John 3:13-17

Friday
1 Timothy 1:1-2, 12-14
Luke 6:39-42

Saturday
1 Timothy 1:15-17
Luke 6:43-49

13
WED

Jayne

Fr John   Absolution +
            Holy Communion

14
THU

New Boiler Fitted

✤ The Triumph of the Holy Cross

15
FRI

Sainsburys with Ali

Alis Mum R.I.P.

16
SAT

read

Peter went up to Jesus and said, 'Lord, how often must I forgive my brother if he wrongs me? As often as seven times?' Jesus answered, 'Not seven, I tell you, but seventy-seven times.

'And so the kingdom of heaven may be compared to a king who decided to settle his accounts with his servants. When the reckoning began, they brought him a man who owed ten thousand talents; but he had no means of paying, so his master gave orders that he should be sold, together with his wife and children and all his possessions, to meet the debt. At this, the servant threw himself down at his master's feet. "Give me time," he said "and I will pay the whole sum." And the servant's master felt so sorry for him that he let him go and cancelled the debt. Now as this servant went out, he happened to meet a fellow servant who owed him one hundred denarii; and he seized him by the throat and began to throttle him. "Pay what you owe me," he said. His fellow servant fell at his feet and implored him, saying, "Give me time and I will pay you." But the other would not agree; on the contrary, he had him thrown into prison till he should pay the debt. His fellow servants were deeply distressed when they saw what had happened, and they went to their master and reported the whole affair to him. Then the master sent for him. "You wicked servant," he said "I cancelled all that debt of yours when you appealed to me. Were you not bound, then, to have pity on your fellow servant just as I had pity on you?" And in his anger the master handed him over to the torturers till he should pay all his debt. And that is how my heavenly Father will deal with you unless you each forgive your brother from your heart.'

Matthew 18:21-35

meditate

"Forgive us our trespasses as we forgive those who trespass against us". Most of us pray these words almost every day. The Gospel gives us an example of the opposite – a parable about how quickly we forget about our Father's mercy and begin to make demands on others. Remember God's love, which is from all eternity.

pray

God of mercy and compassion, you forgive all our guilt and heal all our wounds; grant, I pray, that I may be merciful as you are and may forgive as you have forgiven me.

act

Forgiveness of sins in this parable is compared with remitting a debt, whether large or small. Think of someone who owes you something and perhaps excuse him or her part, or even the full amount they owe you.

SEPTEMBER

As I walked out the door toward the gate that would lead to my freedom, I knew if I didn't leave my bitterness and hatred behind, I'd still be in prison.

ATTRIBUTED TO NELSON MANDELA

17
SUN

Sunday Independent

Home Mission Day

18
MON

2.20 P.S.A Phone Call

19
TUES

Marie — Eye Clinic

20
WED

Sainsburys

21
THU

Twin 8-12   SHOWER PUMP

NOT DONE   THEY SAYS BUT

I DIDNT HEAR THEM

RE BOOKED

22
FRI

SHOWER PUMP. FIXED BY

DUBLIN ELECTRICIAN.

ALL popped in for a cuppa

23
SAT

September

F S S M T W T F S S M T W T F S S M T W T F S S M T W T F S
1 2 3 4 5 6 7 8 9 10 11 12 13 14 15 16 17 18 19 20 21 22 23 24 25 26 27 28 29 30

read

Jesus told this parable to his disciples: 'The kingdom of heaven is like a landowner going out at daybreak to hire workers for his vineyard. He made an agreement with the workers for one denarius a day, and sent them to his vineyard. Going out at about the third hour he saw others standing idle in the market place and said to them, "You go to my vineyard too and I will give you a fair wage." So they went. At about the sixth hour and again at about the ninth hour, he went out and did the same. Then at about the eleventh hour he went out and found more men standing round, and he said to them, "Why have you been standing here idle all day?" "Because no one has hired us" they answered. He said to them, "You go into my vineyard too." In the evening, the owner of the vineyard said to his bailiff, "Call the workers and pay them their wages, starting with the last arrivals and ending with the first." So those who were hired at about the eleventh hour came forward and received one denarius each. When the first came, they expected to get more, but they too received one denarius each. They took it, but grumbled at the landowner. "The men who came last" they said "have done only one hour, and you have treated them the same as us, though we have done a heavy day's work in all the heat." He answered one of them and said, "My friend, I am not being unjust to you; did we not agree on one denarius? Take your earnings and go. I choose to pay the last-comer as much as I pay you. Have I no right to do what I like with my own? Why be envious because I am generous?" Thus the last will be first, and the first, last.'

Matthew 20:1-16

meditate

"The vineyard of the Lord is the House of Israel and the people of Judah his pleasant planting" (Is 5:7). We are the heirs of this prophecy, we are the vineyard of God. He now sends us to work. That is, to tend and care for one another. Whenever we start, there is plenty of work for all.

pray

God and master of the vineyard, you do not want us to be idle but rather you invite us to collaborate with you. Open my eyes to see the needs of my brothers and sisters, and give me a willing heart to work for the salvation of all.

act

Perhaps you know someone who has been out of work for some time. Think of a way of encouraging him or her, or even give them practical help to look for a job.

SEPTEMBER

You have not lived today until you have done something for someone who can never repay you.

ATTRIBUTED TO JOHN BUNYAN

24
SUN

John & Walter chat in yard

25
MON

Sainsburys with Ali
Posted Ellies Birthday card

26
TUES

Ellies Birthday 1995

TRAIN STATION FOR £10 for Jayne.

FOUND MISSING HEARING AID

Sunday	Monday	Tuesday	Wednesday	Thursday	Friday ✝	Saturday
Isaiah 55:6-9	Ezra 1:1-6	Ezra 6:7-8, 12, 14-20	Ezra 9:5-9	Haggai 1:1-8	Daniel 7:9-10, 13-14	Zechariah 2:5-9, 14-15
Philippians 1:20-24, 27	Luke 8:16-18	Luke 8:19-21	Luke 9:1-6	Luke 9:7-9	or Revelation 12:7-12	Luke 9:43-45
Matthew 20:1-16					John 1:47-51	

27 WED

28 THU

Jayne.

Walk Bruoyan St.

Channel 81

CHANNEL 81

29 FRI

HOLY COMMUNION

MASS CARD FOR ALISTAIR

SAINSBURYS

✠ SS Michael, Gabriel and Raphael, Archangels

30 SAT

FLU JAB

TAXI THERE & BACK

read

TWENTY-SIXTH SUNDAY IN ORDINARY TIME

Jesus said to the chief priests and the elders of the people, 'What is your opinion? A man had two sons. He went and said to the first, "My boy, you go and work in the vineyard today." He answered, "I will not go", but afterwards thought better of it and went. The man then went and said the same thing to the second who answered, "Certainly, sir", but did not go. Which of the two did the father's will?' 'The first' they said. Jesus said to them, 'I tell you solemnly, tax collectors and prostitutes are making their way into the kingdom of God before you. For John came to you, a pattern of true righteousness, but you did not believe him, and yet the tax collectors and prostitutes did. Even after seeing that, you refused to think better of it and believe in him.'

Matthew 21:28-32

meditate

John the Baptist appears as someone who poses questions to people around him. Hearing his message and seeing the way he lived should not have left people unquestioned. When we meet people living radical choices, what is our reaction?

Lord Jesus, you invite us to be an example to others of your presence. Grant me integrity of life, so that by my words and actions I may bear witness to you.

act

Think of the things you have committed to do and for whatever reason have left undone. If possible, try to fulfil what you said you would do.

OCTOBER

Teach me to serve you as you deserve; to give and not to count the cost.

ANONYMOUS

1
SUN

2
MON

~~10.50~~
DR PRAKASH
[illegible]
[illegible]

3
TUES

10.50 DR PERKASH

INCREASED MIRTAZAPINE TO 40mg.
BACK AGAIN IN 4 WEEKS.

Sunday	Monday	Tuesday	Wednesday	Thursday	Friday	Saturday
Ezekiel 18:25-28	Zechariah 8:1-8	Zechariah 8:20-23	Nehemiah 2:1-8	Nehemiah 8:1-12	Baruch 1:15-22	Baruch 4:5-12, 27-29
Philippians 2:1-11	Luke 9:46-50	Luke 9:51-56	Luke 9:57-62	Luke 10:1-12	Luke 10:13-16	Luke 10:17-24
Matthew 21:28-32						

OCTOBER

4
WED

5
THU

Bateman St Walk.

6
FRI

Great chat with Jaz

Tim & Julie moved into new flat

M & S shopping

Walked back.

7
SAT

read

Jesus said to the chief priests and the elders of the people, 'Listen to another parable. There was a man, a landowner, who planted a vineyard; he fenced it round, dug a winepress in it and built a tower; then he leased it to tenants and went abroad. When vintage time drew near he sent his servants to the tenants to collect his produce. But the tenants seized his servants, thrashed one, killed another and stoned a third. Next he sent some more servants, this time a larger number, and they dealt with them in the same way. Finally he sent his son to them. "They will respect my son" he said. But when the tenants saw the son, they said to each other, "This is the heir. Come on, let us kill him and take over his inheritance." So they seized him and threw him out of the vineyard and killed him. Now when the owner of the vineyard comes, what will he do to those tenants?' They answered, 'He will bring those wretches to a wretched end and lease the vineyard to other tenants who will deliver the produce to him when the season arrives.' Jesus said to them, 'Have you never read in the scriptures:

> It was the stone rejected by the builders that became the keystone. This was the Lord's doing and it is wonderful to see?

'I tell you, then, that the kingdom of God will be taken from you and given to a people who will produce its fruit.'

Matthew 21:33-43

meditate

The Lord puts us in charge of some part of his vineyard. That is, he sends us to look after it for the good of all. We, like the people in the parable, want to give up the tenancy and become the owners at any cost, even by harming those who are above us.

pray

Lord and master of the field, who call us to work for you, make me mindful of my own responsibilities towards you and those you send my way. Take away from my heart any unnecessary ambition.

act

Consider the way you treat those who are above you at work or at home. You might consider changing your attitude or amending your behaviour.

OCTOBER

The desire to reach for the stars is ambitious. The desire to reach hearts is wise.

MAYA ANGELOU

8
SUN

9
MON

MEDICINE 8   DELIVERED

HAIRCUT
SAINSBURYS
BUS THERE & BACK.

10
TUES

ALIS MARY TO ST MARYS

Sunday	Monday	Tuesday	Wednesday	Thursday	Friday	Saturday
Isaiah 5:1-7	Jonah 1:1 – 2:1, 11	Jonah 3:1-10	Jonah 4:1-11	Malachi 3:13-20	Joel 1:13-15; 2:1-2	Joel 4:12-21
Philippians 4:6-9	Luke 10:25-37	Luke 10:38-42	Luke 11:1-4	Luke 11:5-13	Luke 11:15-26	Luke 11:27-28
Matthew 21:33-43						

11
WED

Jayne

Toe nails

Funeral.

12
THU

Train Station for cash.

13
FRI

Sainsburys   Ali

14
SAT

Bateman St.

read

Jesus said to the chief priests and elders of the people: 'The kingdom of heaven may be compared to a king who gave a feast for his son's wedding. He sent his servants to call those who had been invited, but they would not come. Next he sent some more servants. "Tell those who have been invited" he said "that I have my banquet all prepared, my oxen and fattened cattle have been slaughtered, everything is ready. Come to the wedding." But they were not interested: one went off to his farm, another to his business, and the rest seized his servants, maltreated them and killed them. The king was furious. He despatched his troops, destroyed those murderers and burnt their town. Then he said to his servants, "The wedding is ready; but as those who were invited proved to be unworthy, go to the crossroads in the town and invite everyone you can find to the wedding." So these servants went out on to the roads and collected together everyone they could find, bad and good alike; and the wedding hall was filled with guests.'

Matthew 22:1-10
(Longer form *Matthew* 22:1-14)

meditate

"Blessed are those invited to the wedding feast of the Lamb." The bible describes heaven as a wedding. Jesus is the bridegroom, who loves us and makes us ready for that feast day. Events come to invite us to this wedding feast, but in the end, whether we accept this invitation is up to us.

pray

God our Father, you desire to enter into a close relationship with us. Make me accept the events of my life and grant me faith to see them as a preparation for what awaits me for all eternity.

act

Some of those invited have excuses to avoid going to the wedding. Many times we also have excuses not to spend time with the Lord. Think of the excuses you make and perhaps try to give them up.

OCTOBER

Do you wish to rise? Begin by descending. You plan a tower that will pierce the clouds? Lay first the foundation of humility.

ATTRIBUTED TO St Augustine

15
SUN

16
MON

WILKINSONS   for light Bulb

Bus there & back

17
TUES

18
WED

NAILS

SAINSBURYS   BUS THERE & BACK.

✤ St Luke, Evangelist

19
THU

~~As I~~

No I got Times instead.

20
FRI

ALI FITTED BULB

SAINSBURYS Sausage & Fish.
LEFT WALLET IN ALI CAR.
TIM HAS BEEN LAID OFF.

21
SAT

ALI Tim & Debby came with wallet

October

S M T W T F S S M T W T F S S M T W T F S S M T W T F S S M T
1 2 3 4 5 6 7 8 9 10 11 12 13 14 15 16 17 18 19 20 21 22 23 24 25 26 27 28 29 30 31

read

The Pharisees went away to work out between them how to trap Jesus in what he said. And they sent their disciples to him, together with the Herodians, to say, 'Master, we know that you are an honest man and teach the way of God in an honest way, and that you are not afraid of anyone, because a man's rank means nothing to you. Tell us your opinion, then. Is it permissible to pay taxes to Caesar or not?' But Jesus was aware of their malice and replied, 'You hypocrites! Why do you set this trap for me? Let me see the money you pay the tax with.' They handed him a denarius, and he said, 'Whose head is this? Whose name?' 'Caesar's' they replied. He then said to them, 'Very well, give back to Caesar what belongs to Caesar – and to God what belongs to God.'

Matthew 22:15-21

meditate

Many coins carry an image representing the person who ordered them made, and whom ultimately they belong to. Sometimes, because of use, that image wears away and the coin's provenance is not clear. Each of us was made to carry the image of God in us, but through our sins that image wears away. Now is the time to have it imprinted on us again.

pray

God, our creator, we thank you for making us in your own image and likeness and for calling us to be your children. Give us grateful hearts so that we may give praise to you for all you do for us.

act

A way of giving our life back to God is by praising him. Perhaps set aside some time to thank God for the things he has given you.

OCTOBER

Sometimes God permits what he hates to accomplish that which he loves.

STEVE ESTES

22
SUN

ORDERED DVDs "The Missing" from
AMAZON

23
MON

SAINSBURYS with Ali

24
TUES

GO TO VISIT MARIE
TAXI THERE AND BACK
VISION NOT GOOD KNEES CAUSING PROBLE
HOLLY & STEPHEN BACK FROM CRETE

Sunday	Monday	Tuesday	Wednesday (England & Scotland)	Wednesday (Wales) ✠	Thursday	Friday	Saturday ✠
Isaiah 45:1, 4-6	Romans 4:20-25	Romans 5:12, 15, 17-21	Romans 6:12-18	Hebrews 11:33-40	Romans 6:19-23	Romans 7:18-25	Ephesians 2:19-22
1 Thessalonians 1:1-5	Luke 12:13-21	Luke 12:35-38	Luke 12:39-48	John 12:24-26 or	Luke 12:49-53	Luke 12:54-59	Luke 6:12-19
Matthew 22:15-21				15:18-21 or 17:11-19			

25
WED

✢ Six Welsh Martyrs and Companions

26
THU

CLEARED LEAVES

27
FRI

Beans + Chips

28
SAT

EGG SANDWICHES

✢ SS Simon and Jude, Apostles

October	S	M	T	W	T	F	S	S	M	T	W	T	F	S	S	M	T	W	T	F	S	S	M	T	W	T	F	S	S	M	T
	1	2	3	4	5	6	**7**	**8**	9	10	11	12	13	**14**	**15**	16	17	18	19	20	**21**	**22**	23	24	25	26	27	**28**	**29**	30	31

read

THIRTIETH SUNDAY IN ORDINARY TIME

When the Pharisees heard that Jesus had silenced the Sadducees they got together and, to disconcert him, one of them put a question, 'Master, which is the greatest commandment of the Law?' Jesus said, 'You must love the Lord your God with all your heart, with all your soul, and with all your mind. This is the greatest and the first commandment. The second resembles it: you must love your neighbour as yourself. On these two commandments hang the whole Law, and the Prophets also.'

Matthew 22:34-40

meditate

Sometimes we are not sure of what loving God and our neighbour means. These two commandments summarise the Decalogue and you could say that in each one of the tablets these two are elaborated. Do this and you shall live!

pray

God of love, you command us to
follow in your footsteps so that we may
experience life; teach me to love you
and to serve my brothers and sisters.

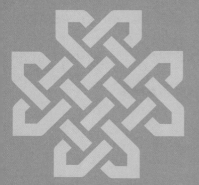

act

The Church teaches us that there are
fourteen ways of loving our neighbour
through the works of mercy. Perhaps
you could pick one and try to put it
into practice.

OCTOBER

The miracles in fact are a retelling in small letters of the very same story which is written across the whole world in letters too large for some of us to see.

C. S. LEWIS

29 SUN

Sausage & Mash

British Summer Time ends – clocks go back

30 MON

COULDN'T STOP WATER GUSHING FROM RADIATOR. JOHN FOUND STOPPER ON FLOOR & FIXED THINGS. Has had been bleeding RADIATOR & GADGET CAME OUT.

DERBY HOMES ARRIVED 7.30 & FIXED EVERY THING. DO NOT BLEED RADIATORS.

Bank Holiday (Rep. of Ireland)

31 TUES

CENTRAL HEATING WORKING DANDY

DR. 12.10 ~~KEEP~~ NO CHANGE

SAINSBURYS BUS THERE & BACK

Halloween

Sunday	Monday	Tuesday	Wednesday ✤	Thursday ✤	Friday	Saturday
Exodus 22:20-26	Romans 8:12-17	Romans 8:18-25	Revelation 7:2-4, 9-14	Isaiah 25:6-9	Romans 9:1-5	Romans 11:1-2,
1 Thessalonians 1:5-10	Luke 13:10-17	Luke 13:18-21	1 John 3:1-3	Romans 5:5-11	Luke 14:1-6	11-12, 25-29
Matthew 22:34-40			Matthew 5:1-12	Matthew 11:25-30		Luke 14:1, 7-11

1
WED

✠ All Saints

£49 Refund from BBC STORE

2
THU

ORDERED 2 PAIRS TROUSERS CHAPS

✠ Commemoration of All the Faithful Departed (All Souls)

SAINSBURYS with ALI

3
FRI

ST JOSEPHS FOR HOLY COMMUNION

ALI ORDERED SHOES FROM CHUMS FOR ME.

TROUSERS DELIVERED

4
SAT

TOO BIG MUST RETURN THEM

read

Addressing the people and his disciples Jesus said, 'The scribes and the Pharisees occupy the chair of Moses. You must therefore do what they tell you and listen to what they say; but do not be guided by what they do: since they do not practise what they preach. They tie up heavy burdens and lay them on men's shoulders, but will they lift a finger to move them? Not they! Everything they do is done to attract attention, like wearing broader phylacteries and longer tassels, like wanting to take the place of honour at banquets and the front seats in the synagogues, being greeted obsequiously in the market squares and having people call them Rabbi.

'You, however, must not allow yourselves to be called Rabbi, since you have only one Master, and you are all brothers. You must call no one on earth your father, since you have only one Father, and he is in heaven. Nor must you allow yourselves to be called teachers, for you have only one Teacher, the Christ. The greatest among you must be your servant. Anyone who exalts himself will be humbled, and anyone who humbles himself will be exalted.'

Matthew 23:1-12

meditate

People said that Jesus taught with authority and not like their scribes. The authority of Jesus comes from a unity between what he said and what he did. The strength of his argument was the humility with which he behaved. Have we got those qualities?

pray

Lord Jesus, you are the only teacher; guide me in ways of sincerity, truth and freedom so I may abide by every word, thought and intention I have.

act

"They do not lift a finger to help those overburdened." Consider people around you and see if anyone is overburdened by something. Perhaps you might be able to give them a hand.

NOVEMBER

The bible tells us to love our neighbours, and also to love our enemies; probably because they are generally the same people.

G. K. Chesterton

5
SUN

6
MON

CUSTOMER SERVICES AT INTU.
(RETURNED) TROUSERS TO CHUTS WITH HIS
HELP.   LUNCH AT DEBENHAMS

7
TUES

271.85

Jayne

TROUSERS   TROUSERS   FROM CHUMS

Sunday	Monday	Tuesday	Wednesday	Thursday ✢	Friday	Saturday
Malachi 1:14 – 2:2, 8-10	Romans 11:29-36	Romans 12:5-16	Romans 13:8-10	Ezekiel 47:1-2, 8-9, 12	Romans 15:14-21	Romans 16:3-9, 16, 22-27
1 Thessalonians 2:7-9, 13	Luke 14:12-14	Luke 14:15-24	Luke 14:25-33	1 Corinthians 3:9-11, 16-17	Luke 16:1-8	Luke 16:9-15
Matthew 23:1-12				John 2:13-22		

8
WED

Jane

9
THU

£267

HEALING PRAYER ENQUIRY
FROT WEB SITE.

✛ Dedication of the Lateran Basilica

£247

10
FRI

REPLACEMENT TROUSERS
DELIVERED

M&S BUS THERE AND BACK

11
SAT

November

W T F S S M T W T F S S M T W T F S S M T W T F S S M T W T
1 2 3 **4 5** 6 7 8 9 10 **11 12** 13 14 15 16 17 **18 19** 20 21 22 23 24 **25 26** 27 28 29 30

read

THIRTY-SECOND SUNDAY IN ORDINARY TIME

Jesus told this parable to his disciples: 'The kingdom of heaven will be like this: Ten bridesmaids took their lamps and went to meet the bridegroom. Five of them were foolish and five were sensible: the foolish ones did take their lamps, but they brought no oil, whereas the sensible ones took flasks of oil as well as their lamps. The bridegroom was late, and they all grew drowsy and fell asleep. But at midnight there was a cry, "The bridegroom is here! Go out and meet him." At this, all those bridesmaids woke up and trimmed their lamps, and the foolish ones said to the sensible ones, "Give us some of your oil: our lamps are going out." But they replied, "There may not be enough for us and for you; you had better go to those who sell it and buy some for yourselves." They had gone off to buy it when the bridegroom arrived. Those who were ready went in with him to the wedding hall and the door was closed. The other bridesmaids arrived later. "Lord, Lord," they said "open the door for us." But he replied, "I tell you solemnly, I do not know you." So stay awake, because you do not know either the day or the hour.'

Matthew 25:1-13

meditate

Wisdom and foolishness are used elsewhere by Matthew to describe those who put the word of God into practice and build their house on rock, and those who do not put the word into practice and build on sand. Wisdom or foolishness are not moral categories, but refer to those who either obey God's command or do not.

pray

Lord Jesus, you invite us to be ready to receive you when you come in to our lives. Grant me a readiness to listen to your word and the will to put it into practice.

act

The invitation is to be ready and to put into practice what the word tells us to do. Think of a word from God that you might want to act on.

NOVEMBER

Aspire not to have more, but to be more.

ATTRIBUTED TO OSCAR ROMERO

12
SUN

£259

Remembrance Sunday

13
MON

£264

SAINSBURYS with Ali

MADE APT with doctor for tomorrow

14
TUES

LEFT MOBILE IN TAXI GOT BUS BACK

TO IN DOCTOR?

PRESCRIPTION FOR BLOOD PRESSURE &
VERTIGO

Sunday	Monday	Tuesday	Wednesday	Thursday (England & Wales)	Thursday (Scotland) ✠	Friday	Saturday
Wisdom 6:12-16	Wisdom 1:1-7	Wisdom 2:23	Wisdom 6:1-11	Wisdom 7:22 – 8:1	Proverbs 31:10-13, 19-20, 30-31	Wisdom 13:1-9	Wisdom 18:
1 Thessalonians 4:13-18	Luke 17:1-6	– 3:9	Luke 17:11-19	Luke 17:20-25	or 1 Corinthians 12:31-13:13	Luke 17:26-37	14-16; 19:6-9
Matthew 25:1-13		Luke 17:7-10			Matthew 25:31-46		Luke 18:1-8

15 WED

£229

CENTRING PRAYER KINDLE DOWNLOADED.

16 THU

£247

LECTIO DIVINA   BASIL PENNINGTON
2

OLD SPICE   FROM AMAZON

✠ St Margaret of Scotland

17 FRI

SAINSBURYS

DOCTOR WITH ALI

B.P STILL HIGH

REAPPOINT FOR NEXT FRIDAY

LEFT SHOULDER XRAY AT DRI
PRESCRIPTION FOR CODINE

18 SAT

VERTIGO STILL A BOTHER £245
HOT EYE COMPRESS DELIVERED. WILL USE NEXT WEEK.

WATCHED 1 SOCCER MATCH & 2 RUGBY - IRELAND BEAT FIJI
ENGLAND BEAT AUSTRALIA

read

Jesus spoke this parable to his disciples: 'The kingdom of heaven is like a man on his way abroad who summoned his servants and entrusted his property to them. To one he gave five talents, to another two, to a third one; each in proportion to his ability. Then he set out.

Now a long time after, the master of those servants came back and went through his accounts with them. The man who had received the five talents came forward bringing five more. "Sir," he said "you entrusted me with five talents; here are five more that I have made."

Matthew 25:14-15, 19-20
(Longer form *Matthew* 25:14-30)

meditate

God has entrusted his most precious property to us: his own Son, given to us in the sacraments. He made us his children in baptism. We receive him in Holy Communion; he forgives us our sins in the Sacrament of Reconciliation. How do we live out our lives after receiving these gifts?

pray

O God, who in your abundance pour
out on us your gifts, make me profit
by your grace so that I may experience
the rewards of your love in my life.

act

Consider the gifts given to you by God,
especially those present in the sacraments
and how you are using them.

NOVEMBER

The person born with a talent they are meant to use will find their greatest happiness in using it.

ATTRIBUTED TO JOHANN WOLFGANG VON GOETHE

19 SUN

£247   REDEMPTORISTS 9.30AM MASS

READING CENTERING PRAYER KINDLE

CENTRAL PRAYER AND INNER AWAKENING DELIVERED FROM AMAZON

20 MON

Limerick Cathedral 10.30 MASS

VERTIGO

Dr BLOOD TEST

21 TUES

£262   ANNE MARIE — HER BACK IS BAD.

Joined W.C.C.M. John Main Meditation Group VIA INTERNET

Sunday	Monday	Tuesday	Wednesday	Thursday	Friday	Saturday
Proverbs 31:10-13, 19-20, 30-31 1 Thessalonians 5:1-6 Matthew 25:14-30	1 Maccabees 1:10-15, 41-43, 54-57, 62-64 Luke 18:35-43	2 Maccabees 6:18-31 Luke 19:1-10	2 Maccabees 7:1, 20-31 Luke 19:11-28	1 Maccabees 2:15-29 Luke 19:41-44	1 Maccabees 4:36-37, 52-59 Luke 19:45-48	1 Maccabees 6:1-13 Luke 20:27-40

£262

Jayne

22
WED

Meditation   6.30 — 7.30

£281

23
THU

Meditation   7.30

1.00

6.30

£265

24
FRI

£292

TABLET ARRIVED

25
SAT

MARION BROUGHT LUNCH

F. FOUNDATION MAKING GREAT PROGRESS

HANNAH LIVING IN ALES TREE

November

W	T	F	S	S	M	T	W	T	F	S	S	M	T	W	T	F	S	S	M	T	W	T	F	S	S	M	T	W	T
1	2	3	4	5	6	7	8	9	10	11	12	13	14	15	16	17	18	19	20	21	22	23	24	25	26	27	28	29	30

read

OUR LORD JESUS CHRIST, KING OF THE UNIVERSE

Jesus said to his disciples: 'When the Son of Man comes in his glory, escorted by all the angels, then he will take his seat on his throne of glory. All the nations will be assembled before him and he will separate men one from another as the shepherd separates sheep from goats. He will place the sheep on his right hand and the goats on his left. Then the King will say to those on his right hand, "Come, you whom my Father has blessed, take for your heritage the kingdom prepared for you since the foundation of the world. For I was hungry and you gave me food; I was thirsty and you gave me drink; I was a stranger and you made me welcome; naked and you clothed me, sick and you visited me, in prison and you came to see me." Then the virtuous will say to him in reply, "Lord, when did we see you hungry and feed you; or thirsty and give you drink? When did we see you a stranger and make you welcome; naked and clothe you; sick or in prison and go to see you?" And the King will answer, "I tell you solemnly, in so far as you did this to one of the least of these brothers of mine, you did it to me." Next he will say to those on his left hand, "Go away from me, with your curse upon you, to the eternal fire prepared for the devil and his angels. For I was hungry and you never gave me food; I was thirsty and you never gave me anything to drink; I was a stranger and you never made me welcome, naked and you never clothed me, sick and in prison and you never visited me." Then it will be their turn to ask, "Lord, when did we see you hungry or thirsty, a stranger or naked, sick or in prison, and did not come to your help?" Then he will answer, "I tell you solemnly, in so far as you neglected to do this to one of the least of these, you neglected to do it to me." And they will go away to eternal punishment, and the virtuous to eternal life.'

Matthew 25:31-46

meditate

At the end of our lives we will be judged by the way we treated the weakest members of society: the hungry, the thirsty, the foreigner, the naked, the housebound, the imprisoned and those who are frail. This is so because Jesus is present in them.

pray

God of mercy, you are slow to anger and abounding in love. Open my eyes to the needs of the weaker members of society, so that in their faces I may see your glorious face.

act

The Gospel suggests some corporal works of mercy. Perhaps pick one and try to put it into practice.

NOVEMBER

Let us really love all men; let us love Christ above all; and then we cannot avoid loving the rightful freedom of others, living in harmony with them.

St Josemaría Escrivá

26
SUN

BENEDICTINE BRIEVARY DELIVERED

7. 30 — 8. 30

1. 00 — 2. 00

6 00 — 7. 00

✣ Our Lord Jesus Christ, King of the Universe

27
MON

248.

28
TUES

222

ALI's DOOR & WINDOW FITTED

SEEDS OF CONTEMPLATION ARRIVED

29 WED

222

TOE NAILS DONE

CLOCK & TABLET CASE FROM AMAZON

30 THU

294

CALENDER & DIARY FROM CTS

BIBLE FROM EDEN

✠ ✠ St Andrew, Apostle and Martyr

1 FRI

MORRISONS   Holy Communion

SILENCES & STILLNESS IN EVERY SEASON

2 SAT

234

December

F	S	S	M	T	W	T	F	S	S	M	T	W	T	F	S	S	M	T	W	T	F	S	S	M	T	W	T	F	S	S
1	2	3	4	5	6	7	8	9	10	11	12	13	14	15	16	17	18	19	20	21	22	23	24	25	26	27	28	29	30	31

read

FIRST SUNDAY OF ADVENT

Jesus said to his disciples: 'Be on your guard, stay awake, because you never know when the time will come. It is like a man travelling abroad: he has gone from home, and left his servants in charge, each with his own task; and he has told the doorkeeper to stay awake. So stay awake, because you do not know when the master of the house is coming, evening, midnight, cockcrow, dawn; if he comes unexpectedly, he must not find you asleep. And what I say to you I say to all: Stay awake!'

Mark 13:33-37

meditate

God's interventions always happen under the cover of darkness: creation happens in the darkness, the exodus from Egypt occurs in the middle of the night, as does the liberation of Peter and Paul from prison. Night is God's favourite time, because when we are at our weakest he shows his might. Stay awake to see him acting!

pray

God of all times, you come to visit us
when we least expect you; open my eyes
to your arrival so that I may experience
the liberating power of your presence.
May I be aware of the ways in which you
come my way.

act

**The night is the favourable time
to meet God. Perhaps think of
how you could spend some time
with God during the night.**

DECEMBER

We are more curious about the meaning of dreams than about things we see when awake.

ATTRIBUTED TO DIOGENES LAERTIUS

3
SUN

7. 30   —   8. 30

1. 00 PM   —   2. 00

6. 00 PM   —   7. 00

4
MON

ADVENT & CHRISTMAS THOMAS MERTON

7. 30

7. 30   —   8. 30

MK.

METER   READING   FOR   BULB

6. 00   7. 00

5
TUES

7. 30   —   8. 30

6. 00   —   7. 00

Sunday	**Monday**	**Tuesday**	**Wednesday**	**Thursday**	**Friday ✠**	**Saturday**
Isaiah 63:16-17; 64:1, 3-8	Isaiah 2:1-5	Isaiah 11:1-10	Isaiah 25:6-10	Isaiah 26:1-6	Genesis 3:9-15, 20	Isaiah 30:19-21, 23-26
1 Corinthians 1:3-9	Matthew 8:5-11	Luke 10:21-24	Matthew 15:29-37	Matthew 7:21, 24-27	Ephesians 1:3-6, 11-12	Matthew 9:35 –10:1, 6-8
Mark 13:33-37					Luke 1:26-38	

DECEMBER

6
WED

£217

7.30 – 8.30

1.00 – 2.00 JAYNE

6.00 – 7.00

7
THU

£326

8
FRI

£341

SAINSBURYS with ALI

✣ Immaculate Conception of the Blessed Virgin Mary

9
SAT

December	F	**S**	**S**	M	T	W	T	F	**S**	**S**	M	T	W	T	F	**S**	**S**	M	T	W	T	F	**S**	**S**	M	T	W	T	F	**S**	**S**
	1	**2**	**3**	4	5	6	7	8	9	10	11	12	13	14	15	**16**	**17**	18	19	20	21	22	**23**	**24**	25	26	27	28	29	**30**	**31**

read

The beginning of the Good News about Jesus Christ, the Son of God. It is written in the book of the prophet Isaiah:

Look, I am going to send my messenger before you;
he will prepare your way.
A voice cries in the wilderness:
Prepare a way for the Lord,
make his paths straight,

and so it was that John the Baptist appeared in the wilderness, proclaiming a baptism of repentance for the forgiveness of sins. All Judaea and all the people of Jerusalem made their way to him, and as they were baptised by him in the river Jordan they confessed their sins. John wore a garment of camel-skin, and he lived on locusts and wild honey. In the course of his preaching he said, 'Someone is following me, someone who is more powerful than I am, and I am not fit to kneel down and undo the strap of his sandals. I have baptised you with water, but he will baptise you with the Holy Spirit.'

Mark 1:1-8

meditate

There is no Christian life without a call to amend our ways. That call comes in different ways, either through words spoken by someone or events happening in our lives – or even the example of others. Amending our life will prepare us for the coming of Jesus.

pray

Lord Jesus, you do not want the death of the wicked man but rather that he be converted and live; grant me conversion of heart so that I may prepare the way for your coming into my life.

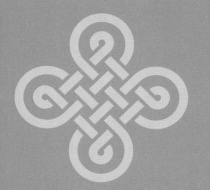

act

The people listening to John the Baptist's message confessed their sins. Perhaps during this Advent you might consider going to confession.

DECEMBER

By failing to prepare, you are preparing to fail.

ATTRIBUTED TO BENJAMIN FRANKLIN

10
SUN

WCCT   Cell Meeting 11.00AM

11
MON

£319

POSTED CHRISTMAS CARD TO
Michael
BUS THERE n BACK.

12
TUES

13 WED

FR JOHN   HOLY COMMUNION
ABSOLUTION

14 THU

HAIR CUT

BUS THERE & BACK.

15 FRI

EE ROUTER ARRIVED

ALI SET IT UP
ALL GOOD.

16 SAT

SOPH & MARIE & STEPHEN   £283

MY MOBILE IS CRACKING UP.
GOT LOAF Na BOOZE

read

A man came, sent by God.
His name was John.
He came as a witness,
as a witness to speak for the light,
so that everyone might believe through him.
He was not the light,
only a witness to speak for the light.

This is how John appeared as a witness. When the Jews sent priests and Levites from Jerusalem to ask him, 'Who are you?' he not only declared, but he declared quite openly, 'I am not the Christ.' 'Well then,' they asked 'are you Elijah?' 'I am not' he said. 'Are you the Prophet?' He answered, 'No.' So they said to him, 'Who are you? We must take back an answer to those who sent us. What have you to say about yourself?' So John said, 'I am, as Isaiah prophesied:

> a voice that cries in the wilderness:
> Make a straight way for the Lord.'

Now these men had been sent by the Pharisees, and they put this further question to him, 'Why are you baptising if you are not the Christ, and not Elijah, and not the prophet?' John replied, 'I baptise with water, but there stands among you – unknown to you – the one who is coming after me; and I am not fit to undo his sandal-strap.' This happened at Bethany, on the far side of the Jordan, where John was baptising.

John 1:6-8,19-28

meditate

"Who are you?" This question posed to John the Baptist is one that we ask ourselves often. "What is your mission?" is another way of phrasing the same question. As Christians our greatest task is to follow John the Baptist's example: to bear witness to Christ, the light which enlightens our world.

pray

Lord Jesus, you are the Word proclaimed and announced to our society. Make me a herald of your message, so that my words and my voice may help spread your word, and many may come to believe in you.

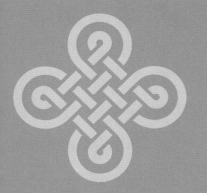

act

As Christmas – the feast day of the True Light – approaches, you might want to have a candle lit at home as a focus of the light of the world coming to us.

DECEMBER

You are still not capable of bearing God's company all the time.
Well, say so. God knows that perfectly well, whatever you do about
it. Go apart, say for a moment, 'I'll just have a rest. For a moment
I accept to be less saintly.'

METROPOLITAN ANTHONY OF SOUROZH

17
SUN

£325

18
MON

belintope for Ali's card

SAINSBURYS

BUS THERE BACK
SPOKE TO PROF MAZ on PHONE.
£334

19
TUES

ALI SAINSBURYS

DOCTOR OSTEO ARTHRITIS

MARIE CALLED HER ME & ALI WALKED
TO HOS.

Sunday
Isaiah 61:1-2, 10-11
1 Thessalonians 5:16-24
John 1:6-8, 19-28

Monday
Jeremiah 23:5-8
Matthew 1:18-24

Tuesday
Judges 13:2-7, 24-25
Luke 1:5-25

Wednesday
Isaiah 7:10-14
Luke 1:26-38

Thursday
Song of Songs 2:8-14
or Zephaniah 3:14-18
Luke 1:39-45

Friday
1 Samuel 1:24-28
Luke 1:46-56

Saturday
Malachi 3:1-4, 23-24
Luke 1:57-66

20
WED

£334

Jayne.

21
THU

ALI TO USA STAYING AT
PREMIER INN TONIGHT FLYING TOMORROW

MAZ WILLIAM ELLIE IZZIE
HERE GREAT TO SEE THEM.

22
FRI

£272

ALI ARRIVED O.K.

23
SAT

Taxi to Jaynes Back
with Plant Christmas Pies
£50 from Michael.

December

| F | S | S | M | T | W | T | F | S | S | M | T | W | T | F | S | S | M | T | W | T | F | S | S | M | T | W | T | F | S | S |
| 1 | 2 | 3 | 4 | 5 | 6 | 7 | 8 | 9 | 10 | 11 | 12 | 13 | 14 | 15 | 16 | 17 | 18 | 19 | 20 | 21 | 22 | 23 | 24 | 25 | 26 | 27 | 28 | 29 | 30 | 31 |

read

FOURTH SUNDAY OF ADVENT

The angel Gabriel was sent by God to a town in Galilee called Nazareth, to a virgin betrothed to a man named Joseph, of the house of David; and the virgin's name was Mary. He went in and said to her, 'Rejoice, so highly favoured! The Lord is with you.' She was deeply disturbed by these words and asked herself what this greeting could mean, but the angel said to her, 'Mary, do not be afraid; you have won God's favour. Listen! You are to conceive and bear a son, and you must name him Jesus. He will be great and will be called Son of the Most High. The Lord God will give him the throne of his ancestor David; he will rule over the House of Jacob for ever and his reign will have no end.' Mary said to the angel, 'But how can this come about, since I am a virgin?' 'The Holy Spirit will come upon you', the angel answered, 'and the power of the Most High will cover you with its shadow. And so the child will be holy and will be called Son of God. Know this too: your kinswoman Elizabeth has, in her old age, conceived a son, and she whom people called barren is now in her sixth month, for nothing is impossible to God.' 'I am the handmaid of the Lord,' said Mary, 'let what you have said be done to me.' And the angel left her.

Luke 1:26-38

meditate

"Let it be done to me according to your word". These words set Mary on a journey into the unknown. She became the Mother of God, went to Egypt, settled in Nazareth, followed her son to the cross and gathered the Church – waiting for the Holy Spirit. Her consent supported her in joyful, glorious and even sorrowful events.

pray

Lord Jesus, in every generation, you choose individuals to show your power. Make me docile to your will, knowing that whatever you want me to do will be for your greater glory and for the salvation of the people of my generation.

act

Prompted by the angel's words, Mary went to visit her cousin; perhaps at this Christmas time you might visit some relation or friend.

DECEMBER

Anyone thinking of the Holy Child as born in December would mean by it exactly what we mean by it; that Christ is not merely a summer sun of the prosperous but a winter fire for the unfortunate.

G. K. CHESTERTON

24
SUN

Anne   Ivor & Tony

25
MON

To Lunch.   Maries for Christmas All very well

Taxi there & Back.

✣ Christmas Day, Nativity of Our Lord

26
TUES

All enjoying USA.

emailed her today

John's Dad ~~died~~ died a few days ago

✣ St Stephen, First Martyr; Boxing Day (Bank Holiday)

27
WED

GOSPELS BOOK ARRIVED.

✛ St John, Apostle and Evangelist

28
THU

MAZ CAME WITH FOOD ON HER WAY BACK FROM TAKING HAMMAM HOME

WE HAD GREAT CHAT - SHE IS DOING GREAT THINGS AND EXPANDING BUSINESS

✛ The Holy Innocents, Martyrs

29
FRI

WALKED TO SAINSBURYS DBL CREAM + TRIFLE + BANANAS
BUS BACK
MADE STEW. VERY NICE

✛ St Thomas Becket, Bishop and Martyr

30
SAT

December

F S S M T W T F S S M T W T F S S M T W T F S S M T W T F S S
1 2 3 4 5 6 7 8 9 10 11 12 13 14 15 16 17 18 19 20 21 22 23 24 25 26 27 28 29 30 31

read

THE HOLY FAMILY OF JESUS, MARY AND JOSEPH

When the day came for them to be purified as laid down by the Law of Moses, the parents of Jesus took him up to Jerusalem to present him to the Lord.

When they had done everything the Law of the Lord required, they went back to Galilee, to their own town of Nazareth. Meanwhile the child grew to maturity, and he was filled with wisdom; and God's favour was with him.

Luke 2:22, 39-40
(Longer version *Luke* 2:22-40)

meditate

"Mary stored up all these things in her heart." How many things Mary must have not understood, but she did not rebel; on the contrary, she kept it all in her heart. Then all made sense when she lost Jesus to death but regained him three days later. Everything in our lives prepares us for later events.

pray

Lord Jesus, you are in the bosom of the Father and have come to reveal to us his presence in our lives. Make me stay close to you so that I may grow in wisdom and knowledge of you.

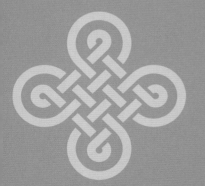

act

Jesus spent extra time in the Temple; during this holiday season, you might contemplate spending some time in a church.

DECEMBER – JANUARY 2018

The object of a new year is not that we should have a new year.
It is that we should have a new soul.

G. K. CHESTERTON

31
SUN

✣ The Holy Family of Jesus, Mary and Joseph

1
MON

✣ Mary, the Mother of God; Bank Holiday

2
TUES

Bank Holiday (Scotland)

Sunday ✣	**Monday** ✣	**Tuesday**	**Wednesday**	**Thursday**	**Friday**	**Saturday**
Genesis 15:1-6, 21:1-3	Numbers 6:22-27	1 John 2:22-28	1 John 2:29 – 3:6	1 John 3:7-10	1 John 3:11-21	1 John 5:5-13
Hebrews 11:8, 11-12, 17-19	Galatians 4:4-7	John 1:19-28	John 1:29-34	John 1:35-42	John 1:43-51	Mark 1:7-11
Luke 2:22-40	Luke 2:16-21					

JANUARY

3
WED

4
THU

5
FRI

6
SAT

Epiphany of the Lord (Ireland)

January

M	T	W	T	F	S	S	M	T	W	T	F	S	S	M	T	W	T	F	S	S	M	T	W	T	F	S	S	M	T	W
1	2	3	4	5	6	7	8	9	10	11	12	13	14	15	16	17	18	19	20	21	22	23	24	25	26	27	28	29	30	31

PRAYERS FOR DIFFERENT OCCASIONS

Prayer in times of insecurity and anxiety

Lord Jesus, in these times of insecurity and anxiety, we are stretched in so many ways, spiritually, physically, financially. People are no longer given their true dignity, and so much that we treasure is gone. It is hard at times to trust. Help us to anchor ourselves in you, whose love for us is unchanging.

May your Spirit lead us in your way. May our hope in you give us the peace of soul you promise. Amen.

Prayer for peace of mind

O Jesus, banish from my mind all anxieties, troubles and fears of any kind. Make my mind calm and serene and fill it only with loving thoughts and confidence in you. Amen.

Prayer for guidance in difficult times

Almighty, eternal, just and merciful God, give us miserable ones the grace to do for you alone what we know you want us to do, and always to desire what pleases you. Inwardly cleansed, interiorly enlightened and inflamed by the fire of the Holy Spirit, may we be able to follow in the footprints of your beloved Son, our Lord Jesus Christ. And, by your grace alone, may we make our way to you, Most High, who live and rule in perfect Trinity and simple unity, and are glorified God almighty, forever and ever. Amen.

Prayer for those with financial difficulty

Lord, you know how difficult it is to make ends meet. Everything seems to be so expensive and it is a constant struggle to keep going. Help me to have hope and provide for us so that I will be less consumed by this gnawing fear that is always with me. Help me to trust you to do this for us. Amen.

Prayer when our fears overwhelm us

Lord, I am often filled with fear when I think of the future. I am haunted by past mistakes and hurts, afraid of what the future might hold and I feel paralysed. I surrender it all to you now. I ask you to heal all that is wounded in me and trust you to take care of all I worry about. You are the one who makes all things new. With you I will go forward, securely and joyfully, into freedom. Amen.

Prayer for those who feel lonely, abandoned or rejected

Dear Lord, sometimes I feel so lonely and seem to get engulfed by these feelings. The more I think about it, the more I get bogged down by it all. Let me experience your deep love for me, so that I may be strengthened in my inner self. Let me find my security in you, so that, even when I am alone, I may not feel this dreadful loneliness. I know that if this sense of being loved by you takes a deep root in my heart, my self-worth will return and I will find it easier to have the confidence to face situations in life that I often avoid now, which leave me feeling lonely. I trust in you – let me not be disappointed. Amen.

Prayer for those suffering with depression

Lord, you know the darkness that envelops me. This cloud descends on me and when it does, I seem to lose all perspective. It seems like it will never lift. I know I have pulled out of it before, but when it starts again, it clouds everything. Help me to trust in you in this difficult time. I know that after the rain, the sun shines again and that above the clouds, the sun is always shining. But please impress this conviction in my heart, so that your gift of hope will carry me through. I believe that you can heal me and so I entrust myself to you. Give me the graces I need to 'hang in there' until your healing love, which I know is constantly working on me, finally penetrates and gives me the relief that I need. Amen.

Prayer for those with marital difficulties

Heavenly Father, I thank you for my marriage partner, for the gift of our married life together. At this point in time, as you know, we are struggling. It can be so painful at times – to be living so closely with someone and yet unable to communicate in a constructive way.

I ask you to come into the situation. You are the third person in our marriage and we need your grace to continue on. Let your Spirit of love and reconciliation renew and deepen our love for each other and help us to grow in trust. We ask this in Jesus' name. Amen.

Prayer for a person suffering from illness

Dear Lord, I ask you to heal me. I feel so wretched and it seems to be constant. When I am submerged by sickness, it takes over and I can think of nothing else. I ask you to lay your healing hands on me and bring me some relief. I believe in your power to heal, which you showed so much when you were on earth. I believe that you want only what is best for me, and so I ask you to give me the graces I need. If it is not your will that I be healed at this time, send your Holy Spirit to comfort and strengthen me and use my suffering to somehow help others. I ask you especially to bless those who are looking after me. I trust in you and your great love for me, and so I leave myself in your hands. Amen.

Prayer for those sitting exams

Lord, I ask you to help me at this stressful time. I feel that so much depends on these exams. I feel that in addition to carrying my own burdens, I am carrying the expectations of so many others – family, friends, society. Help me to keep calm at this time, so that I can think straight and apply myself to the best of my ability. Let your Spirit help and inspire me so that I can remember all that I have studied and put together my answers in the best way. Guide me in all my ways so that I will find fulfilment in you. Amen.

BASIC PRAYERS

Our Father

Our Father, who art in heaven,
hallowed be thy name;
thy kingdom come,
thy will be done
on earth as it is in heaven.
Give us this day our daily bread,
and forgive us our trespasses,
as we forgive those who trespass against us;
and lead us not into temptation,
but deliver us from evil.
Amen.

Hail Mary

Hail, Mary, full of grace, the Lord is with thee.
Blessed art thou among women,
and blessed is the fruit of thy womb, Jesus.
Holy Mary, Mother of God,
pray for us sinners,
now, and at the hour of our death.
Amen.

Glory be to the Father

Glory be to the Father, and to the Son,
and to the Holy Spirit.
As it was in the beginning, is now,
and ever shall be, world without end.
Amen.

The Apostles' Creed

I believe in God,
the Father almighty,
Creator of heaven and earth,
and in Jesus Christ, his only Son, our Lord,
who was conceived by the Holy Spirit,
born of the Virgin Mary,
suffered under Pontius Pilate,
was crucified, died and was buried;
he descended into hell;
on the third day he rose again from the dead;
he ascended into heaven,
and is seated at the right hand of God
    the Father almighty;
from there he will come to judge
    the living and the dead.
I believe in the Holy Spirit,
the holy catholic Church,
the communion of saints,
the forgiveness of sins,
the resurrection of the body,
and life everlasting.
Amen.